A GUIDI
THE INDUSTRIAL
ARCHAEOLOGY
OF TYNE AND WEAR

Compiled by

Ian Ayris
Tyne and Wear Specialist Conservation Team

and

Stafford M. Linsley
Lecturer in Industrial Archaeology,
Centre for Continuing Education,
University of Newcastle upon Tyne.

Design by George Tullin
Cover by Steve Urwin

Published by the Tyne and Wear Specialist Conservation Team, Development Department, Newcastle upon Tyne City Council in association with Gateshead Metropolitan Borough Council, North Tyneside Council, Borough of South Tyneside and the City of Sunderland.

1994

ISBN 1 85795 026 7

Jesmond Old Mill, Newcastle upon Tyne c1890.

INTRODUCTION

From the mid eighteenth century until the Second World War industrial development was of such immense importance to the region that the surviving industrial heritage forms a highly significant element of the history and environment of the present day Tyne and Wear area. The period of industrial activity was indeed long and the decline has been recent but it would be wrong to assume that the surviving industrial archaeology of the area contains and records the full story of that development. In fact the surviving industrial buildings, machines, structures, earthworks and artefacts reflect the continuing change within the present-day environment as much as the industrial past. The factors which have determined the survival of sites are diverse - location, size, adaptability to reuse, etc,- and have generally little to do with the relative importance to the region of the structure or the industry of which it was once a part. Consequently whilst the coal industry has been far and away the most dominant influence on the development of the region for over four hundred years, reclamation schemes, in particular, have reduced coal mining and coke manufacturing sites to a mere handful. However, the past is not to be denied - the transport routes and the engineering achievements which followed in the wake of, and grew with, the burgeoning coal industry are still an intrinsic part of the landscape. Many remarkable nineteenth century bridges survive and are still in use, the routes of the eighteenth and nineteenth century waggonways and railways have survived in parts of the County where neither urban expansion nor opencast mining has disturbed the landscape. Along the river banks the story is different. The riverside industries of the late eighteenth and early nineteenth centuries, for example, the Tyneside chemical industry, were overlaid in the following hundred years by a plethora of heavy engineering, shipbuilding and repairing yards which themselves have now all but disappeared. The removal of redundant plant and the reclaiming of the river corridors for new uses has left only threadbare patchwork remains of what was once a rich tapestry of activity along the two rivers. Generally throughout the region the changing economic structure, urban sprawl, opencast mining and pressure upon land has sadly brought the loss of irreplaceable elements of the former industrialised economy and environment.

Categorisation of the existing remains is difficult and contentious even within a simple guide book. A coal staith could equally well be categorised as part of the coal industry, as part of the railway which served it or as a facility of the river where it was situated. To overcome some but by no means all anomalies of this kind related topics have been grouped into sections - thus for example railways, the riversides, bridges, roads, warehouses and street furniture form one section, agriculture, food and drink production and wind and water mills such as Jesmond Old Mill (opposite), form another. Whilst this is not meant to be a comprehensive gazetteer of the industrial archaeology of the County, an attempt has been made to look in detail at some structures, focusing within each subject on one or more of the most significant sites, and giving briefer coverage of other examples throughout the County.

Locations

All entries have been given either a National Grid Reference or where more appropriate a street address. Generally buildings set within heavily urbanised areas and smaller items, for example milestones, are identified by a street name, whereas structures and features such as railways and bridges have been given six figure grid references. Each section has a focus upon a main site, after which sites are listed within the different districts of the County.

Tyne and Wear County Districts

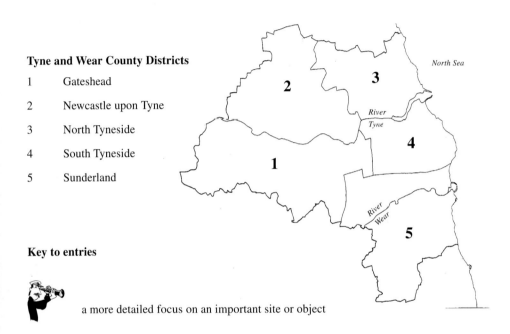

1   Gateshead

2   Newcastle upon Tyne

3   North Tyneside

4   South Tyneside

5   Sunderland

Key to entries

a more detailed focus on an important site or object

➤   publicly accessible site - either permanently or on open days

★   visible from a public highway or footpath

Acknowledgements

Gazetteers are by their nature eclectic. Many of the entries, particularly the more technically detailed ones, are the work of Stafford Linsley, others have been compiled by Ian Ayris and some have been drawn from other sources based on the work of some of the region's leading local historians and specialists, in particular Neil Sinclair on Sunderland, Frank Manders on Gateshead, Norman McCord on the Tyne, Bob Rennison on the water industry, Barbara Harbottle on the archaeology of the County and Grace McCombie and Peter Jubb on its historic architecture. These direct and indirect contributions are gratefully acknowledged.

The Industrial Archaeology of Tyne and Wear : Contents

R A I L W A Y S

THE BOWES RAILWAY, SPRINGWELL, SUNDERLAND. NZ 259568 to NZ 299609. ➤

From early in the seventeenth century, in an attempt to carry coal from the mines to navigable water, the Great Northern Coalfield generated increasingly more complex railway systems with ever increasing efficiency. Until the second half of the eighteenth century, horses and gravity were the sole means of propelling the wagons along the wooden ways. From then on however a series of improvements were introduced in the North East. Better brakes, better track, dandy wagons, self acting inclines, stationary hauling engines and finally locomotives, ushered in a new breed of railway.

The Bowes line, as it has been called since 1932, was one such line. From staiths at Jarrow it was opened to Springwell and Mount Moor in 1826, being engineered by George Stephenson. In 1842 it was extended to Kibblesworth and by 1855 it had linked with other railways as far as Pontop and became known as the Pontop and Jarrow Railway. The line reached an ultimate length of fifteen miles, had seven rope worked inclines and three loco-worked sections. As collieries closed, the line gradually reduced in size until closure came with the demise of Kibblesworth Colliery in 1974. At its closure three stationary electric haulers, one gravity inclined plane and diesel locomotives were all used; this being the last such system in Great Britain.

Bowes Railway: locomotive No. 22 at Springwell Yard.

Special features of the line are the Blackfell and Blackham's stationary haulers and their associated inclines. The Blackfell engine rope-hauled full wagons up from the bottom of the Team Valley and lowered empties at the same time. The Blackham's engine took up the full wagons at Blackfell and drew them up to the summit. It also lowered empties back down, but in separate operation. Moreover it also worked the Blackham's East incline down to Springwell, the hauler having two separately clutched winding drums. Both of these engine houses originally housed steam powered haulers and signs of that system can still be seen in the provision of water, coal sidings, reused boilers etc. Stone sleeper blocks edge the tracks near Blackham's West crossing and the rope sheaves, pulleys, kip and dish system, rope marks, jack points etc. can all be studied here.

Springwell Yard is the foot of the Blackham's East incline from which the full wagons passed to the head of the Springwell self acting incline plane where descending full wagons were used to pull empties back up. Springwell Colliery was located to the east of the tracks in the yard and the site of one of the shafts can still be determined. The former coal store for that colliery, a heavily buttressed building, was converted to a wagon repair shop when the colliery closed. On the opposite side of the tracks are the railway and coal mine repair shops.

Railway systems such as these were born and nurtured in the North East and gave George and Robert Stephenson and other great railway engineers their earliest railway building and operation experience. This section of the Bowes Railway, which is a Scheduled Ancient Monument, is managed by a voluntary body - The Bowes Railway Company Limited - on behalf of Sunderland and Gateshead District Councils. It is the world's only preserved standard gauge rope-hauled railway. The Bowes Railway Company arrange regular public open days providing steam train rides and displays of the rope haulage.

The Bowes Railway: Blackham's Hill Engine House.

Gateshead

Brandling Railway Station, Felling,
NZ 276621. ★
Disused stone built station of 1842 on the 1839 railway planned by the Brandling family. A small chapel-like station with a tall narrow projecting cross gable towards the track side having triple lancet windows, above which is the family crest and the prophetic initials 'BR'.

Gateshead East and West Stations,
NZ 253634. ★
Little remains of these stations other than their approaches, that to the east station being particularly interesting in that it climbs up beneath the viaduct from an imposing entrance. This station also had a good footbridge, and some ornamental cast-iron work but its platform buildings were fairly plain.

Greenesfield Locomotive Works, Gateshead,
NZ 251633. ★
The hotel off Hudson Street, originally built in the 1840s for the Brandling Junction Railway and the former boiler shop dating from the late 1870s on Rabbit Banks Road survive. Constructed in stone and two-storeys, increasing to three-storeys as the hill slopes down, the shop is an impressive sight from the riverside below. It is now used for vehicle repairs. The Greenesfield Works was for many years the largest employer in the town. It was opened in the 1850s and by the early years of the present century over 3,000 men relied on it for their livelihood. But the cramped site limited its expansion and in 1910 locomotive building was transferred to a new works at Darlington. Locomotive repairing continued at Greenesfield until 1932 when that ceased also; the works reopened during the Second World War but was finally closed in 1959. The Station Hotel of 1844 is a stone building whose

unmodified facade to the north is plain, with 7 bays and a hipped roof. Adjacent are some pre-1856 works buildings with arcaded extension and good internal structural cast iron work; later additions, mainly of the 1880s, extended the works to the west. The range of buildings overlooking the steep river banks represents a dramatic high level feature. Most of the buildings remain in use although not all for railway purposes.

Oakwellgate Station, Gateshead,
NZ 256636. ★
Formerly the West terminus of the Brandling Junction Railway and now a scrapyard, but the gracious inclined approach drive suggests that the station buildings, of which only fragments remain, may have been quite imposing. The north end of the yard is built up on a high, arched retaining wall and at the east end of this the inclined railway down to the Tyne can still be traced.

The Tanfield Railway, Marley Hill,
NZ 208573. ➤
The Tanfield Railway was in a sense the successor to the Tanfield Waggonway of 1727 which, having lain dormant for several decades, was taken over on a wayleave agreement in c1835 by the Brandling Junction Railway Company which began to relay track from Tanfield Lea to Dunston on Tyne in 1837, completing the job by 1840. By securing the coals of Tanfield Lea colliery they dealt the coup de gras to the Stanhope and Tyne Railway which thereby lost some £5,000 annual revenue. The Tanfield Railway rose some 536 ft from the Tyne in 3.25 miles before descending 90 ft over the next 2.25 miles to Tanfield Lea colliery and then rising once more to its terminus at over 800 ft AOD at Tanfield Moor Colliery (by 1841). With gradients varying between 1 in 12 and 1 and 454, several changes in motive power were necessary along the route - engine planes, self-acting planes and

horse planes. Horses continued to work the more level sections until 1881. In 1842 the DJR commenced passenger operations on the section of the line between Tanfield Lea and Gateshead; up and down the inclines, on Saturdays only. This was not uncommon on the rope-worked railways of County Durham in the 1840s. In 1844 the BJR was bullied into settling terms with the infamous George Hudson for the sale of their line and branches to him personally although within days he transferred it to his Newcastle and Darlington Junction Company and the Tanfield Railway thereby became part of the NER in 1854.

The 1825 Springwell Waggonway from Jarrow to Springwell Colliery had been extended to Kibblesworth Colliery in 1842 but ten years later it was acquired by John Bowes and Partners who had already taken over Marley Hill Colliery in 1847. To obtain a cheaper route to the Tyne for their Marley Hill coals which had previously been taken by the Tanfield Railway, the Bowes Company decided to extend its line from Kibblesworth to Marley Hill and beyond in 1855, thereby depriving the Tanfield line of the Marley Hill and other coals, losing, it was estimated, some £20,000 per year, a reversal of the Tanfield's earlier attack on the Stanhope and Tyne. The Tanfield's proprietors, now the NER, must have been particularly galled that the Bowes line crossed theirs at right angles on a level crossing. Such were the tangled webs of railway competition!

Just to the west of the crossing the Bowes Company built a loco shed. With the closure of the south end of the Tanfield line in 1962 and the rest of it two years later, followed by the closure of the Marley Hill section of the Bowes line in 1969, this shed became the focus for a railway preservation society which has amassed a variety of rolling stock and has an ongoing programme for re-laying the level sections of the old Tanfield Railway. They, like

the BJR nearly 150 years before them, run passenger services on summer Sundays, but not down rope worked inclines.

Pelaw Main Railway. ➤
Another once extensive railway system of the early nineteenth century using the same techniques as those on the Bowes Railway. During its last years Pelaw Main traffic was brought via a new connection onto the Blackham's East incline of the Bowes Railway. One spur of the Pelaw Main had passed under the Blackfell Incline at NZ 278576 and its routes can be followed from here. The last part of the Pelaw Main to close (1973) ran from Lady Park Drift (NZ 242588) to Allerdene Incline bank foot (NZ 253587), this section being worked by locomotive over a concrete viaduct through the Team Valley Trading Estate. The Kings Engine (NZ 266581) worked the Allerdene Incline to the site of the Ravensworth Ann Colliery, and the Seven Stars Engine (NZ 272594) worked the incline up to the summit. From here the system was latterly locomotive worked to Blackham's East (NZ 283583) and Springwell Yard (NZ 285587).

Locomotive Shed, Wardley, NZ 299697. ➤
Forming part of the Bowes Railway Ancient Monument, Wardley Loco Shed, at the foot of Springwell Incline marks the end of the former rope worked sections of the railway and the start of the more level route to Jarrow worked by locomotives. The building is a robust stone structure with a relatively modern metal framed, cladded shed attached. Presently used by the North East Bus Preservation Society.

Newcastle

Jesmond Railway Station, NZ 254653. ➤
Disused since 1977 and now 'The Carriage' public house and restaurant this former station on the Blyth and Tyne railway dates from 1864 and was probably built to the design of J F Tone. A good example of a small suburban station in Tudor style, single storey in red brick with stone dressings, strong cross gable on platform side, some mullioned windows, octagonal chimney stacks etc.

Kenton & Coxlodge Waggonways. ➤
The historic development of the waggonways in this district is quite complex and little survives other than the alignments of these eighteenth century waggonways. For example Fawdon Park Road, The Meadows and Jubilee Road from NZ 223692 to 240680 is the alignment of an 1809 branch, whilst Waggonway Road and possibly Regent Farm Road represent an 1813 modification - NZ 239686 to 252683. Beyond here the route is easy to follow between NZ 257681 and 290665. It was on this route that Blenkinsop introduced rack rails and locomotive in 1813.

Newcastle Central Station, NZ 246638. ➤
An important monumental station with classical frontage by John Dobson, although his total conception was never fulfilled entirely. Built mainly by 1850, the massive portico with arched openings was added in 1863 to a design by Thomas Prosser and not to Dobson's original design. West of the portico the straight frontage terminates in a later revenue accountants office with an arched door opening and pediment above. To the East, the 1892 Royal Station Hotel of six storeys maintains the classical style but has a glazed entrance canopy with good cast iron tracery incorporating the letters NER. Behind this long and straight frontage lies one of the most important train sheds in the country, its roof utilising for the first time, arched wrought iron beams to support the roof cladding of timber with glazed ridge ventilators. The original roof has three 60' (18.3m) segmental spans, the central span being somewhat higher than the outer two. The whole is aligned on a distinct curve giving platforms of up to 1335 ft (407 m) long. In detail the main curved wrought iron beams were formed from built up I beams fishplated together to give a full span. Every third rib is supported on plain tapered cast iron columns except at the junction with the rear of the station frontage, which is curved on the inside although straight on the outside. Here the ribs are supported on pilasters located between the arcades which form the rear of the station offices. The cast-iron columns have two tier cross girders which support the intermediate arch rib. The trainsheds were extended to the south with less adventurous but still quite elegant arches in 1894. Note complete diamond junction at east end of main station.

Quayside Branch, Newcastle, NZ 255644 to NZ 259641. ★
A short branch line of the NER opened 1870 with gradients as steep as 1 in 27, falling 130 ft (40 m) in less than 1 mile (1.6 km) in cutting or tunnel all the way linking the Quayside with the main line near New Bridge Street. Electrified c1904, dieselised 1964, closed 1969. Tunnel portal still visible at NZ 259641.

Locomotive Works, South Street, Newcastle, NZ 247637. ★
The site was first developed in c1821 at a time of industrial expansion on the west side of Newcastle city centre. The development, on land leased from the Hospital of St. Mary the Virgin, was known as Forth Street after the new service road to the site. The first building was erected in South Street as a foundry by Isaac

& John Burrell. George Stephenson was a partner in the firm. The locomotive and general engineering firm, in his son's name, Robert Stephenson & Co., was founded on the adjacent site in 1823. The Stephenson Company premises were the World's first locomotive factory. The company became one of the premier manufacturers of locomotives and other steam engines in home and overseas markets.

The pre -1830 development occupied the east side of South Street. The buildings survive, albeit with partial alteration to roofs and interior layout. The site on the west side of South Street underwent progressive development and alteration throughout the nineteenth century. The main years of development were 1837, 1846, 1855 and 1867. The Burrell foundry site was absorbed in 1867.

Robert Stephenson & Co. Ltd. left the site in 1902 having established a new factory in Darlington. The various leases and premises were acquired by the General Post Office who occupied the oldest buildings (being the former Burrell's premises) and by R & W Hawthorn, Leslie & Co., the locomotive and marine engine company of the adjacent Forth Banks site, who absorbed the major part of the site to the west of South Street.

The Stephenson Company returned to the site in 1937 on its merger with Hawthorn, Leslie. The manufacture of industrial locomotives by Robert Stephenson & Hawthorns Ltd. and its successors continued at the enlarged Forth Banks works to the west of South Street. Production at the site ceased in 1960 and the site was released for other purposes.

Whilst many of the buildings are incorporated within a DIY retail warehouse, No. 20 South Street survives relatively intact. It includes parts of the former offices but more

significantly it features an important fully glazed wall which gave light into what was the boiler manufactory. The building is currently held by the Robert Stephenson Trust who are looking to develop the site as a museum to the life and works of one of the country's foremost engineers.

Victoria Tunnel, NZ 237657 to NZ 263641.

A 'subterranean railway' using gravity to take full wagons from Spital Tongues Colliery down to the Tyne near Glasshouse Bridge, the empties being returned by stationary steam engine haulage. The tunnel is part stone and part brick arched with a masonry invert arch and runs through clay at a maximum depth of 85' (26 m) on its one and a half mile (2.4 km) journey. It was constructed 1839-42 to avoid the longer overground route around the built up city centre, but was closed and offered for sale by 1857 without takers. Re-used as air raid shelters during 1939-44 war. Once briefly considered for mushroom cultivation a length of the tunnel is now used as sewer. However the stretch from New Bridge Street to Ouse Street and the length running parallel with Claremont Road survive undisturbed and are reasonably dry and well ventilated.

Victoria Tunnel in use as an air raid shelter during World War II.

North Walbottle Railway. ➤

When Blucher Colliery (NZ 177661) opened c1815 a new line was laid with a self-acting inclined plane down to the Tyne at Lemington. This line was extended to Coronation Pit (NZ 177673) in c1827 partly along the line of the old Holywell Reins Waggonway (q.v.). Both of these collieries closed in 1867. In 1892 North Walbottle Colliery was sunk and the line was reopened and extended to the colliery (NZ 181681) again partly along the line of the older waggonway. At the bottom end the line was rerouted onto the Scotswood to Newburn Line of the NER which had opened in 1876.

In 1901 Blucher Pit reopened but used an endless rope tubway to take coals to a screening plant at Newburn (NZ 175652), the tubway being extended parallel to the North Walbottle Colliery and Railway which closed in 1968. A right of way exists along the railway and interesting points are the original route to the staiths (NZ 181648 to NZ 184644), the bankhead of the self acting inclined plane where remains of the cabins, dish and kips can be detected (NZ 177655), a branch line to Newburn from NZ 176659, the tubway passing under the railway at Blucher Colliery and the two running together between Blucher and Coronation Pits.

Holywell Reins Waggonway, Walbottle.

Like the Walbottle Moors Waggonway this was heading for the river Tyne near Lemington (NZ 187644) but the only easily discernible section until recently was the field boundaries in a near straight line between NZ 182687 and NZ 195695. This horse drawn way was in operation by 1767 but appears to have closed by 1800. Nevertheless part of its alignment was later used by collieries on the North Walbottle Railway.

Walbottle Moors Waggonway. ➤

A late 18th century horse drawn waggonway system on which George Stephenson was employed when a boy, in keeping the tracks clear of livestock. The way had three or four branches on the fell to the north of Walbottle, all coming together before Cut End at NZ 166675 and almost all still existing as public rights of way with shallow embankments to Callerton Lane End (NZ 160687) Broomhall Farm (NZ 167692) and Black Callerton (NZ 177696). The whole of this area abounds with shallow pit workings and of special interest is a section of waggonway (NZ 173689) where rig and furrow ploughing has obliterated the waggonway which may have been in operation until c 1815. To the south of Cut End the way has a short section with adverse gradient.

Wylam Waggonway, NZ 165652. ➤

Alongside and to the North of the 1876 Scotswood, Newburn and Wylam Railway alignment is the track of the 1748 Wylam Waggonway on which Thomas Hedley used locomotives from 1813. Originally a five mile long waggonway linking Wylam Colliery with staiths at Lemington, built possibly to the design of Thomas Brown of Throckley for John Blackett. Laid to a 5ft gauge using timber rails attached to stone sleeper blocks. Much of the waggonway was incorporated into the later S, N & W. Railway which worked until 1968.

Waggonway Bridge, former Wylam Waggonway, Newburn, NZ 173651. ➤

A surviving masonry skew bridge formerly carrying the Wylam Waggonway over the New Burn, probably dating from the mid to late eighteenth century. The later Scotswood, Newburn and Wylam Railway Bridge over the burn stands immediately adjacent to the structure which, after the closure of the waggonway, took a branch line from the S, N & W to Spencer's Newburn Steel Works.

North Tyneside

Avenue Branch Line, NZ 339756. ➤

The Avenue Branch Line of the Blyth and Tyne Railway, the route of which is still clear striking northward from Whitley Bay toward Old Hartley, was laid in 1860 following in part the route of the Whitley Waggonway, opened in 1811 carrying coal from Whitley Old Pits to North Shields and closed in 1850.

Backworth, Cramlington and Seghill Colliery Railways, NZ 291737 to NZ 332680. ➤

A series of once important colliery railways swept in parallel through the Shiremoor area on their way to the Northumberland Dock, Whitehill Point and the Albert Edward Dock. The railway corridor formed by these lines is still clearly visible along much of its route. The history of the routes is complex but briefly the Backworth route was opened in 1818 and by 1827 was worked principally by rope haulage from Backworth Colliery. The Cramlington line opened in 1823 and was added to as the mines around Cramlington were opened out, notably at Shankhouse and East Hartford. The Seghill Colliery line opened in 1839.

Blyth and Tyne Railway, NZ 295742 to NZ 325688. ★

The Blyth and Tyne was formed to link the rivers Blyth and Tyne. Constructed from 1845 to 1847 with a number of extensions and additions in following decades. Beginning life as a colliery railway linked in to the Seghill Railway near Seaton Delaval it soon became a major artery of the coalfield. By 1857 it had a coal handling staith in Northumberland Dock and was becoming an important passenger handling railway. It was vested into the NER system in 1874.

George Stephenson's House - 'Dial Cottage', Forest Hall, NZ 276706. ➤

Inhabited by George Stephenson 1805-1823, a $1\frac{1}{2}$ - storey cottage in stone with red pantiles which may have been three separate cottages.

George Stephenson's House, Forest Hall.

Killingworth Waggonway. ★

Famous in the Annals of George Stephenson and laid at 4'8" (1.4m) gauge in 1806, two years after he was taken on at Killingworth West Moor Colliery. On this line Stephenson experimented with fixed engines. Little of the line survives except for an alignment between NZ 283700 (?) and NZ 310685 with some earthworks.

Seaton Burn Railway, NZ 238738 to NZ 248724. ➤

This section opened in 1837 being a branch of the 1826, 5ft 6 ins gauge Brunton and Shields line, built by Benjamin Thompson, to use fixed engines and ropes, the success of which caused Walker and Raistrick to recommend a similar system for the Liverpool and Manchester Railway. The line from the Seaton Burn junction to Burradon (NZ 270722) is part of the original route but is difficult to follow between Burradon and the Tyne.

Tynemouth Railway Station.

Tynemouth Station, NZ 366693. ➤

The Newcastle and North Shields Railway was first opened in 1839 between a terminus in Carliol Square, Newcastle and the present station site at North Shields. In 1847, this line was extended, as part of the then Newcastle and Berwick Railway, to a new terminus in what is now Oxford Street, Tynemouth. The structures involved were designed by John and Benjamin Green, and their building at Tynemouth in a Tudor Gothic style still survives, along with an adjacent later classical building.

Meanwhile, the Blyth and Tyne Railway was extending its system, and in 1860-61 opened a branch from near Hartley to a terminus of its own on the north side of the main Tynemouth Road, some 500 yards to the West of the earlier site. This site is also still extant, but as a station was succeeded in 1864 by a temporary site a little way to the N.E. of its predecessor, on a

short new spur. In 1865 this in turn was superseded when the spur was extended to a third station on a site just to the north of the other company's terminus. Meanwhile in 1864 this company had also opened its own route to Newcastle, terminating in New Bridge Street, and running from the junction at Monkseaton via Backworth and Jesmond.

Eventually, however, the Blyth and Tyne was taken over by the North Eastern Railway, of which the direct route was by this time a part. As such from 1874 the whole complex, still physically separated at Tynemouth, was owned by the one company. A grand reorganisation was almost bound to occur, therefore, bearing in mind the extent to which the railway network had developed nationally by this time, and this was completed on 3rd July, 1882.

A new line, on a new alignment altogether, was constructed from a junction on the original Newcastle to Tynemouth route some 300 yards west of its terminus curving northwards to run almost parallel to the Blyth and Tyne route, but some 600-700 yards nearer the coast, and returning to the Blyth and Tyne at Monkseaton. A continuous loop was thus completed, and the older line was subsequently abandoned, except for the short section at the Tynemouth end which was linked to the new route to maintain access to the original Blyth and Tyne station site still in use as a depot. The first 1847 terminus was also retained for coal and goods etc, but the site of the third Blyth & Tyne station is no longer discernible.

A new station at Tynemouth was provided and in the grand manner. It was to be an important station, having a large number of both terminating and through trains, and fit to serve a now considerable seaside resort. Indeed for many years, long distance through trains brought excursion and holiday traffic notably from Glasgow. Thus there are four bay platforms to the south and three to the north, and between the two through platforms there are two additional tracks for the running round of locomotives and the shunting of stock. There is both a north and a south signal box and the extensive goods facilities already indicated.

Architecturally, the station buildings are a delight, reflecting the prominence of the seaside traffic. The major part of the passenger platforms are roofed over with an iron and glass canopy of almost 200 yards in length, and an extravagance of ornamentation is lavished in the cast iron brackets and the general detailing throughout. An important central feature of the platform areas is the footbridge over to the smaller western portion of the station, and the quality of ironwork applies also to this, as it does to the barrier railings and lesser fittings. The whole combines to make a station concourse of considerable virtuosity and distinction. The solid buildings of the street frontage, housing the ticket office, waiting rooms, toilets, administrative rooms, etc, are again carefully designed, and are in a sort of Victorian Venetian style. A symmetrical main frontage of about 80 yards length is presented to Station Terrace, and its slightly subdued spirit only hints at the delights that await within. The buildings are generally of red brick with slate roofs, but having a stone cornice and stone dressings with a slightly polychromatic gothic flavour, and the skyline features a great number of chimneys and, of course, ornamental iron cresting along the stonework of the column capitals, drip mouldings and the like, especially internally, complements the glass and ironwork. Another interesting though slightly later, detail is the map of the whole of the North Eastern Railway's network, executed in ceramic tiles, and built into the wall of the passenger concourse.

West Monkseaton Station, NZ 336719. ➤
Railway station in a modernistic 1930s style with curved flanking entrance bays and a flat roof hidden behind parapets. Metal framed windows with a horizontal emphasis on the glazing bars are also typical of the period.

Whitley Bay Station, NZ 358718. ➤
Built for the NER and opened in 1910, the station and train shed being the work of NER engineer William Bell. Built in brick with Welsh slate roof in a Free Baroque style the one storey building runs along 25 bays. The central block has a three stage tower over the entrance porch.

South Tyneside

Marsden Railway Line, NZ 405644 to NZ 380663. ★
Formerly a colliery line built in the 1870s by the Harton Coal Company but extensively rebuilt when the present road was constructed in 1926. From then until 1953 the line also carried passengers between Westoe Lane and Whitburn Colliery, the colliery-standard platelaying generating the line's affectionate epithet, 'The Marsden Rattler'.

South Shields Station, NZ 363673. ➤
A "plain modest building" by William Bell and dating from 1879, is included largely because it houses a glazed tile wall map of the North Eastern Railway network. The map dates from c1905 and is on the east wall of the train shed immediately to the north of the public entrance. It shows items and places of historic interest on the routes and has inset plans of docks at Hull, Hartlepool and Middlesbrough, as well as the Tyne and Northumberland Docks. It consists of 64 tiles framed by a moulded border of gold coloured tiles and signed by the makers.

Stanhope and Tyne Railway. ➤

The Stanhope and Tyne was an ambitious scheme designed to bring limestone from Weardale and coal from North West Durham to the Tyne at South Shields. The first limestone was moved from the Stanhope Limekilns in 1834. The line was 33 $^3/_4$ miles long, over half of which was worked by incline, the level stretches being originally worked by horses. The railways drops were located near what is now the Shields Ferry terminal in what was until recently Brigham & Cowan's Shipyard. The drops fell out of use when the Tyne Dock opened in the late 1850s. The railway approached South Shields via Boldon and Brockley Whins (NZ 629350) in which area the route can still be followed. Through the Districts of South Tyneside and Sunderland and into County Durham the route has been brought back into use as a footpath and cycleway.

Sunderland

Durham and Sunderland Railway. ➤

The Durham and Sunderland railway was authorised in 1834 to connect the two towns. Running from a terminus near the South Docks in Sunderland the line to Haswell was formally opened in 1836, worked by stationary winding engines. It was taken over by Hudson's Newcastle and Darlington Junction Company in 1846 but was still using ropes as late as 1858. The Sunderland to Durham service ran until 1931 after which the route was foreshortened to Pittington. This last service closed in 1953. The junction of what became the NER Sunderland to Hartlepool line and the Durham Elvet and Murton Branch was at Murton Junction (NZ 382494).

Durham Junction Railway, NZ 317552 to NZ 312470. ➤

The DJR was formulated in 1833/34 to run from the Stanhope and Tyne Railway at Washington to Durham, crossing the River Wear at Fatfield. The original plan did not come to fruition but it did achieve the construction of the Victoria Viaduct (q.v.), the cost of which being one of the principal reasons why the scheme was not completed. The line was later taken over by George Hudson as part of his Newcastle and Darlington Junction complex and it was in this form that it finally reached Durham in 1844. Prior to this it had terminated in Rainton Meadows.

Hetton Colliery Railway. ➤

This was the first long line engineered by George Stephenson, opening in 1822, some 3 years before the better known Stockton & Darlington Railway; designed to use steam locomotives where gradients were appropriate and inclined planes where locomotives could not be used. When it opened it used two stationary engines for $1^1/_2$ miles (2.4km) five self acting inclines for about 3 miles (4.4km) and locomotives for $3^1/_2$ miles (5.6km) although fixed engines later replaced locomotives on 2 miles (3.2km). Thus Hetton coals were taken over difficult terrain to staiths on the Wear near Sunderland. The whole of the line is now closed but can be traced at various places in the Hetton area. For example the track alignment can be followed through Hetton-le-Hole as a back street running parallel to and east of the main road through the village (NZ 353476 to 350490), which section was locomotive worked. The stationary engine sections can also be traced from the latter point up to near the watershed at NZ 361500, although quarrying activity is eating into the track. The 1836 (second) Warden Law hauling engine on this line which was formerly at NZ 369505 is now in store at the Open Air museum at Beamish.

Londonderry Railway. ➤

Totally disused and similar in concept to the Hetton Colliery Railway although more complex. It carried Lord Londonderry's coals from mines around Hetton, firstly down to Fatfield on the Wear but then to Seaham Harbour from 1831. One of its branches worked the North Hetton Colliery at Moorsley (NZ 342463) until 1896 and then the Hetton Railway was linked to it until final closure in 1917; the track bed can be clearly seen. This section was worked by a stationary engine which was demolished some years ago. Another good section of trackbed is from Warden Law Farm (NZ 366498) down "The Long Run" to Seaton Bank Top (NZ 392493) although this section closed in 1896. This section was locomotive worked and the loco shed has been incorporated into the farm buildings.

Monkwearmouth Railway Station, NZ 396576. ➤

Designed by Thomas Moore, a local self-taught architect, for George Hudson, the 'Railway King' and M P for Sunderland. Opened 1848 as terminus for Brandling Junction Railway of 1839 which was slightly realigned for the purpose. One of the finest small monumental stations - its massive ionic portico is flanked with Doric devices. Its importance declined after 1879 when the line was extended over the River Wear to Sunderland via the Wearmouth Bridge (q.v.). Rescued from incipient decay and converted into a museum which retains the booking office installed in 1866 and now maintained in 1900 NER style. Note also 1879 footbridge and 1848 Goods depot on west side of track. Overall roof removed 1928.

Monkwearmouth Railway Station

B R I D G E S

THE TYNE BRIDGES

New Tyne Road Bridge, NZ 254638. ➤

Built 1925-28, designed by Mott, Hay & Anderson with R Burns Dick as architect and Dorman Long of Middlesbrough as contractors. Newcastle's modern-day symbol was first proposed in 1921, to augment existing road and tram provision at high level and to provide a job creation scheme. The Corporations of Newcastle and Gateshead, in anticipation of a 65 per cent government grant toward construction, obtained an Act of Parliament in 1924. Work commenced in 1925. Special construction techniques were needed as the Tyne Improvement Commissioners insisted on full navigational clearance, both height and width, throughout the work and thereafter; they also claimed to be anxious to have the Swing Bridge removed and the High Level Bridge rebuilt with larger spans to make river traffic easier. The demand for full navigational clearance required a single span bridge with a level deck and the designers in effect came up with a reduced version of the bridge they had already designed for Sydney Harbour - a two-hinged steel arch of 531 ft (161.4 m) span with a suspended road deck at 84 ft (25.5 m) above high water; massive concrete foundations support abutments for the hinges and the huge, Cornish granite faced pylons above, which are of minimal structural significance, were designed to house warehouses (never used as such) and goods and passenger lifts. The Newcastle approach road is carried on continuous steel girders supported by two pairs of octagonal steel columns, each pair being skewed to accommodate the existing street plan below. Cast-iron balustrades and lanterns by MacFarlane & Co of Glasgow. The largest single-span bridge in Britain at the time of opening.

Tyne Swing Road Bridge, NZ 253637. ➤

Built 1868-76 by W G Armstrong & Co with the Tyne Improvement Commission. At the time of its opening the largest such bridge in the world. It was a necessary development to allow for upriver navigation by sea-going vessels but required the removal of Mylne's nine-arched stone bridge of 1781. Armstrong's also constructed the superstructure but the Commissioners were responsible for the foundations and abutments. A 592 ft (180 m) temporary bridge aided the work which commenced in 1864 with the removal of the Mylne bridge. The wrought-iron superstructure, which is 281 ft (85.6 m) long and weighs 1,450 tons, is supported centrally on cast-iron rollers and gives two 95 ft (29 m) river openings. The whole is driven by the original Armstrong Hydraulic engines but in 1959 small electric pumps replaced the steam pumps which once raised the hydraulic accumulators to store the hydraulic energy. The bridge, which swings only rarely now, is controlled from the attractive cupola above the superstructure. All services, water, once gas and now electricity, are brought down the central pier of the High Level Bridge. Since it began life in 1876 nearly half a million ships have passed through.

The Swing Bridge still in use in 1994.

High Level Bridge, NZ 251637. ➤
Built 1845-49 by Robert Stephenson with T E Harrison. A superb example of Stephenson's use of materials appropriate to their function. Its design followed at least nineteen different proposals by such as Samuel Brown, Robert Stevenson, John Green, John Dobson and I K Brunel, for both high and low level bridges to augment a low level bridge built to the design of Robert Mylne in 1781. The final impetus was the need to link the railway from Darlington to Gateshead with the Newcastle and Berwick Railway, necessarily at high level. In 1845 the decision was taken to build a combined road and rail bridge giving 120 ft (36.5 m) clearance above low water. In its overall length of 1,400 ft (425.6 m) it approached the scale of Stephenson's Britannia Tubular Bridge but here with long spans of 125 ft (38 m), with smaller land arches. Masonry piers on massive timber piles (first use of Nasmyth's steam hammer for piling) support the main spans each of which consists of four cast-iron ribs of I section tied with wrought-iron chains; the rail deck above is supported by cast-iron columns rising from the main ribs while the road deck is slung from the ribs by wrought-iron hangers encased in cast-iron box sections to match the columns above. The main ribs were cast by Hawks Crawshay of Gateshead. Few changes have occurred since it opened except for additional road suspension rods to strengthen the structure to take tramcars in 1922, and more recently gantries relating to the electrification of the main East Coast line.

King Edward VII Rail Bridge, NZ 247633. ★
1902-6 by Charles A Harrison for the North Eastern Railway with Cleveland Bridge and Engineering Co as contractors. The original plan was for two lattice girder spans with land approach arches until it was discovered - surprise, surprise - that old coal workings at both ends meant that most of the arches had to be abandoned. Consequently the bridge was built with four massive steel lattice girder spans carrying four rail tracks, each 28 ft (8.5 m) deep and up to 300 ft (91 m) long, supported on solid stone piers; cost just over £500,000 and very much a workaday design.

Queen Elizabeth II Metro Bridge, NZ 248634. ★
1976-80 by W A Fairhurst & Partners with Cementation Construction Ltd and Cleveland Bridge and Engineering Co as contractors. Through steel truss construction with fabricated box chords; three unequal spans with a total length of 1,184 ft (360 m).

Redheugh Road Bridge, NZ 245631. ★
1980-83 by Mott, Hay & Anderson in association with Tyne and Wear County Council and built by Nuttall/HBM to replace a steel truss bridge of 1897-1901. The most striking of the new Tyne bridges and a good example of modern medium-span bridge design. A post-tensioned concrete box construction with four traffic lanes and one footpath over three spans totalling 1,184 ft (360 m) in length, the main span being 526 ft (160 m), and a 1,161 ft (353 m) approach viaduct on the North side. Internal ducts within the box sections carry gas, water, electricity and telephone services with portholes in the box sections to prevent possible explosions; piers fluted to suggest lightness. Contract value was £15.35 m.

Scotswood Road Bridge, NZ 199636. ➤

1964-67 by Mott, Hay & Anderson and constructed by Mitchell Construction/Dorman Long to replace a suspension bridge of 1831 by John and Benjamin Green. A steel arch of 330 ft (100.5 m) span with suspended box girder deck, the two arch ribs originally tied with wire cables which rapidly corroded and were replaced with tie bars. A very lively bridge which has regularly been repaired and modified since it opened; come back John and Benjamin Green.

Scotswood Rail Bridge, NZ 197639. ★

The present bridge, now disused, is the third on this site. The first, of 1839, was by John Blackmore for the Newcastle and Carlisle Railway, a timber truss bridge on the skew with eleven spans each of 60 ft (18.2 m); it burned down in 1860 during a Board of Trade inspection. A temporary bridge replaced it and lasted until 1871 when the present bridge, with wrought-iron hog-back girders each of 127 ft (38.6 m) on cast-iron cylinder piers, was opened.

Newburn Road Bridge, NZ 165653. ➤

A simple, steel, lattice girder bridge with riveted trusses, supported on concrete filled cylindrical, wrought-iron piers braced in pairs. There are four main spans, the river piers being at 103 ft (31.5 m) centres; 18 ft (5.5 m) wide road deck at about 21 ft (6.4 m) above high water mark. Built in 1893 for the Newburn Bridge Company by Head Wrightson of Thornaby on Tees to the design of Messrs. J W Sandeman & J M Moncrieff of Newcastle to incorporate a 22 in (0.56 m) water main on either side of the bridge; formerly a toll bridge with its toll house at the NE end long demolished.

Redheugh Bridge: The original version built in 1870 to the design of Thomas Bouch and replaced in 1901.

Gateshead

Newcastle

Lintzford Road Bridge, NZ 148570. ➤
Small stone bridge of 2 segmental arches with projecting string course at parapet base and pointed cutwaters. By John Green and therefore probably 1830s but with none of the panache of his Blackwell Bridge at Darlington.

Lintzford Paper Mill Bridge, NZ 150572. ➤
A remarkable stone-built road bridge with single, very flat segmental arch whose voussoirs noticeably increase in size from crown to springings. Projecting string course at tangent to crown, carries parapet. Each spandrel pierced four times with diminishing circular holes in the style of Edward's 1756 bridge at Pontypridd. Bridgehouse of three storeys on east side.

Swalwell Suspension Foot Bridge, NZ 201625. ➤
Wire ropes slung from steel beam towers to give a span of about 121 ft (37 m) and a timber deck width of 5 ft (1.5 m). Rope adjusting clamps at anchorage by Rowell of London. Presumed late 19th or early 20th century but recently renovated. Stone abutments of earlier bridge about 16 ft (5 m) downstream.

Swalwell Old Bridge, NZ 199624. ➤
An attractive stone bridge of c1778 of three segmental arches giving a total span of about 150 ft (45.7 m) with pointed cutwater curved up to half hexagonal retreats which are also corbelled and panelled. Road width about 15 $^3/_4$ ft (4.8 m) between parapets. Now used for access only.

Swalwell Water Pipe Bridge, NZ 199624. ➤
Quaint structure with fancy riser towers faced in stone and a lattice girder bridge with ornate spandrels, built to carry cast iron water pipe across the Derwent, (c1880?).

Armstrong Bridge, NZ 262661. ➤
A unique structure designed and constructed 1876-78 by W G Armstrong & Co. with Messrs. W E and F Jackson as masonry contractors. Eight equal wrought-iron lattice girder spans give an overall length between abutments of 552 ft (168 m), supported by seven pairs of square wrought-iron box-section columns, cross-braced with wrought-iron ties and resting on rock-faced sandstone piers; abutments of similar stone construction. What makes it special are the rocker bearings at the foot and head of each column, the sliding bearings at the central columns and the fact that each girder is separately supported, all to provide articulation to compensate for any mine subsidence and thermal variation; clearly a wise precaution for in the 1970s a trial boring between the east columns was unhappily directly on a mine shaft! The bridge provided high level crossing of Jesmond Dene linking Jesmond and Heaton. At a maximum height of 65 ft (20 m) above the dene it gave a splendid view of the landscape which Armstrong transformed into a park before donating both park and bridge to the Corporation of Newcastle. Pedestrianised in 1960 it has subsequently become the setting for a successful Sunday arts and crafts market. Threatened with demolition in the 1970s but rescued in the 1980s thanks to a late-discovered underspend by central government in 1982. Columns replaced with steel replica cast-iron pilasters replaced in plastic etc. An even more welcome series of repairs to the bridge was undertaken by the City Engineer in 1993/94.

Byker Road Bridge, NZ 262646. ➤
Byker Road Bridge was constructed in 1878 and overcame the need to descend and ascend the steep sides of the Lower Ouseburn Valley. The bridge gave access to the developing eastern suburbs of the city and improved the principal route to the river mouth and coastal area - the Shields Road. A toll was charged for its use until 1895.

Crawford's Bridge, Lower Ouseburn, NZ 262647. ➤
Crawford's bridge is the oldest of the surviving bridges crossing the Lower Ouseburn. It was built in the early to mid eighteenth century of coursed, squared sandstone and is " listed " as a structure of architectural or historical interest. The name of the bridge derives from Thomas Crawford who owned a number of properties in the area in the early nineteenth century.

Dean Street Viaduct, NZ 251639. ★
A finely constructed 80 ft (24.4 m) elliptical span which is in fact only part of a long viaduct from Newcastle Central Station (q.v.) to Manors Station. Built in 1848, but widened to the north in 1894 on a slightly larger span.

Another part of the viaduct takes the form of an iron bridge (NZ 250639) with diamond grid bracing in the spandrels, built by Abbots of Gateshead in 1849. Subsequently widened to the north.

Ouseburn Rail Viaduct, NZ 261647. ★
Like its sister viaduct on the Newcastle and North Shields Railway at Willington (q.v.) the present viaduct is a closely copied 1869 reconstruction in wrought iron, of the original laminated timber viaduct constructed by John Green in 1837-39; Green pioneered the structural use of laminated timber in this country, both for bridges and roof trusses, using techniques which were later to be emulated by such as Locke, Vignoles and Brunel. The viaduct is 918 ft (280 m) long having four stone approach arches, including an accommodation arch over Stepney Road, and five main arches carrying the deck at a height of 108 ft (33 m) above the stream. The reconstruction retained the original stone approaches and piers, these having been designed with possible reconstruction as a conventional viaduct in mind, and repeats the three arch ribs and openwork spandrel bracing of the original.

Crawford's Bridge (foreground) with the Ouseburn Rail Viaduct in the background, c. 1960.

North Tyneside

Sunderland

Salter's Bridge, Longbenton, NZ 254686. ➤
A medieval road bridge of two spans, one
pointed arch having 3 ribs. Later widening to
the south with a segmental arch and added
parapets. A Scheduled Ancient Monument, the
bridge crosses the Ouseburn which here forms
part of the boundary between Newcastle and
North Tyneside.

**Burn Closes Bridge, St Peter's Road,
Wallsend, NZ 309670.** ➤
A reinforced concrete bridge of c1913, listed
Grade II, spanning Willington Dene. Five
trestles and curved abutments support the road
deck. The only early ferro-concrete bridge in
the County.

Willington Viaduct, NZ 316666. ★
The Willington Viaduct was completed for the
Newcastle and North Shields Railway in 1839.
The engineers responsible for its design were
John and Benjamin Green, of Newcastle. The
viaduct was unusual in being of laminated
timber arch construction to the Wiebeking
system. It comprises seven spans, of up to 128
ft to centres; the height of the track above
foundation is 82' 0". The original viaduct
comprising timber arches each consisting of
14 layers of timber 22" x 3 $\frac{1}{2}$" held by trenails,
was built by Messrs. Robson. The timber arches
were replaced by iron in 1869, the contractors
then being the Weardale Iron and Coal
Company.

**Queen Alexandra Bridge, Sunderland,
NZ 382578.** ➤
The Queen Alexandra Bridge was designed by
Charles A Harrison, nephew of Robert
Stephenson's assistant, and constructed by Sir
William Arrol & Co, builders of the Forth Rail
Bridge. The need for the rail bridge was to
avoid coal trains having to reverse at
Washington and Penshaw, thus connecting the
coalfields of Annfield Plain and Washington
with Sunderland's South Docks. Negotiations
between the North Eastern Railway Company
and Sunderland Corporation resulted in an
agreement to build the bridge over the River
Wear in 1899. The approaches were completed
by 1907, by Mitchell Brothers of Glasgow, the

Queen Alexandra Bridge.

subcontractors. By 1909 the Bridge was complete and was ceremoniously opened by the Earl of Durham.

A temporary cantilever principle was utilised in erecting the bridge, a unique and remarkable technique at the time. The footings are of Norwegian granite based on solid clay whilst the arches were of red sandstone, shipped to the Wear from Lockarbriggs Quarry, Dumfriesshire. Structurally the Queen Alexandra Bridge has a centre span three times heavier than that of the Forth Rail Bridge. The 330 feet centre span stands some 85 feet above high water level, it is connected to two 200 feet side spans to the North and one 200 feet land span to the South. Steel is used throughout the latter. The following quantities of material were used: 350,000 bricks; 8,500 tonnes of steel; 60,000 tonnes of red sandstone; and 4,000 tonnes of granite.

Although primarily a rail bridge, facilities were also made for a road and pathways on the lower deck, with gas and water mains flanking the upper deck. During the peak years some six million tonnes of coal passed over the rail deck yearly, however passenger traffic on this route never materialised. Consequently, due to the fall in coal exports, the upper deck closed to regular rail traffic in 1921 leading to the bridge's regrettable epitaph as a 'white elephant'. Following a period of use for wagon storage the semi-redundant rail deck was used as a platform for searchlights and anti-aircraft guns during World War Two.

Wearmouth Railway Bridge, NZ 397574. ★
Wrought iron box girder bowstring bridge of two cross-braced ribs giving single span of 300 ft (91.44 m) at 86 ft (26.2 m) above high water; masonry approach viaducts. An otherwise dull bridge, relieved by oval openwork stiffening webs. Opened 1879 and led south to rail tunnels totalling 1,000 yards (914.4 m) in

length on approach to Sunderland station. The bridge is best seen from a moving bus on the adjacent road bridge.

Wearmouth Road Bridge, NZ 397574. ➤
A 3-pinned steel arch bridge with two parabolic ribs. Masonry faced concrete abutments; single span of 375 ft (114.3 m) at c. 90 ft (27.5) above high water level. Designed by Mott Hay and Anderson and constructed by Sir Wm. Arrol & Co Ltd, it was opened in 1929. Plaque on upstream balustrade at south approach tells how this bridge replaced the famous cast-iron bridge by Rowland Burdon, erected 1796, vastly modified by Robert Stephenson in 1858 and finally demolished in 1929. While it survived it was the largest cast-iron span at 236 ft (71.9 m).

Victoria Viaduct, Washington, NZ 320545. ★
An important viaduct built 1836-8 unusual in its use of large spans. Its four main arches are unequal but the largest is 160 ft (48.7 m) and was the largest span in Europe at the time of building, in its combination of height and span. There are three approach arches of 20 ft (6.1 m) span on either side giving a total length of 820 ft (249.9 m). The height from low water to the underside of the main arch is 120 ft (36.5 m). Its design was based on the Roman Alcantara bridge in Spain whose main arch is 200 ft (60.9 m) above the flow of its valley. Alcantara's builder claimed that it would remain for ever and it still exists. The Victoria Viaduct introducing a Roman scale of operations to the railway era was justly regarded as one of the wonders of the railway age. It remains in use but little known.

RIVER, SEA AND SHIPS

THE MOUTH OF THE WEAR, SUNDERLAND.

The Wear Piers, NZ 411582, NZ 416581. ★

Entering the River Wear from the sea was once a hazardous and treacherous business. Rocks, sandbars and sandbanks made the narrow navigation channels particularly difficult. The water was shallow and becoming even shallower as collier ships brought in ballast and discharged it into the river before filling up with their precious cargo of coal for the London and overseas markets. By the early 1700s these difficulties were restricting the movement of the burgeoning coal shipping trade of the Wear. To improve navigation and facilities on the river, the River Wear Commissioners were established in 1717. Their intention was to maintain and improve the course of the river from Biddick to the sea. With money raised through duties on coal and cinders (more familiar to us as " coke ") , work was soon able to start on the construction of the South Pier. Construction began in 1723 and continued through the following decades. At this time the river had two navigable channels, one nearer the north bank and one nearer the south bank. With the construction of the South Pier, the southern channel (known as the " Sledway ") was opened out and became the main shipping channel.

In the late eighteenth century work began on building a North Pier. The project commenced in 1786 and was completed in 1797, although the piers did not reach their final form until further work was undertaken in the 1840s. The building of the old South Pier was the first major act of the River Wear Commissioners. The construction of the massive outer piers was to be their last. These long curving piers dominate the river mouth to this day. The northern Roker Pier was built between 1885 and 1903 under the supervision of Henry Wake, using huge concrete blocks faced with Aberdeen Granite. The new South Pier was left unfinished in 1907.

The Wear Lighthouses, NZ 407597, NZ 417587. ★

To grace the old North Pier, the Commissioners positioned a splendid lighthouse at its seaward end. Built of stone and designed by Jonathan Pickernell, it stood in this position from 1802 until the 1840s when it was moved bodily and erected at the end of the newly extended North Pier. This remarkable task was performed under the supervision of the Chief Engineer to the Commission, John Murray.

In 1856 a fine wrought iron lighthouse was built on the old South Pier. At the top of the tower was a cast iron dome and internal access to the light was by a cast iron staircase. The 50ft. high structure was designed by Thomas Meik who also designed the Hendon Dock and one of the nearby dock-side grain warehouses, which survived until the early 1990s. The lighthouse itself can also be seen today - but not in its original position. The house was dismantled and re-erected in 1983 when the Sunderland Port Authority shortened the pier to create an easier and safer entrance into the river. Public concern led to the resiting of the structure on the Roker sea front.

The Aberdeen Granite lighthouse built at the end of the Roker Pier at the turn of the century still stands in its proud position guarding the entrance to the Wear.

The North and South Docks, NZ 407584, NZ 412567. ★

The massive increase in shipping activity on the River Wear, brought about by the seemingly ever-expanding coal trade, was causing great congestion on the river by the beginning of the nineteenth century. By the 1820s pressure on the riverside facilities was immense and trade was being lost to rival port facilities. As a result, competing schemes were formulated for docks to be built on the north and south banks to handle the increased traffic.

In 1837 the North Dock was opened by the Wearmouth Dock Company, formed by Sir Hedworth Williamson, the major landowner in Monkwearmouth and Whitburn. The engineer for the project was perhaps the most famous of the Victorian age, Isambard Kingdom Brunel. The dock, however, was too small to be of any significance and its importance was diminished by the building of docks on the south side of the river.

The South Dock was opened in 1850 by the Sunderland Dock Company, headed by George Hudson, the " Railway King " who became one of Sunderland's two Members of Parliament in 1845. The South Dock included the staiths of the Durham and Sunderland Railway, which formed part of Hudson's Railway Empire. A major part of the capital for the Dock was supplied by the

The Old North Pier at the mouth of the River Wear in 1990.

York, Newcastle and Berwick Railway Company. The design of the Dock was by John Murray, the River Wear Commission Engineer. Robert Stephenson, son of George and highly acclaimed in his own right as one of the leading engineers of the day, was employed as a consultant.

In 1859 the Sunderland Dock Company sold out to the River Wear Commissioners who had been able to levy port dues on the dock traffic and thus financially crippled the Company. In the late 1860s the Commissioners added the Hendon Dock, designed by Thomas Meik, as a southern extension. The original dock became known, from this time, as the " Hudson Dock".

In 1922 the River Wear Commissioners gained control of the North Dock from the North Eastern Railway. Whilst never as successful as the south side docks, the North Dock was used for timber and lime loading. The Eastern side was filled in during 1953 to provide a quay for vessels being repaired at Greenwell's Yard. In 1976 a bulk loading conveyor, used principally for limestone, brought a surge of activity to the North Dock. Further modernisation took place in the early 1980s when roll on - roll off facilities were installed.

Of the major dock buildings of the Wear, the North Dock Offices of 1834, attributed to John Dobson, were demolished in 1979, whilst the two South Dock Grain Warehouses were demolished in 1992. The larger of the two warehouses dated from 1856 and was designed by John Dobson, the smaller was designed by Thomas Meik in 1863.

The former 1856 South Pier Lighthouse, now standing on the Roker sea front.

Newcastle

The Ouseburn, NZ 262647. ➤
This was one of the early areas of the industrial development of Newcastle, along with the Skinnerburn to the west of the town. Both of these had the advantages of being beyond the town walls, being a source of water power and having direct access to the river. The Ouseburn was navigable probably as far as Crawford's Bridge (q.v.) and is still used as moorings up to and beyond the Ouseburn Bridge at Cut Bank.

Elswick Wharf, NZ 238628. ➤
A now truncated but repaired and accessible timber wharf which dates from the nineteenth century and was previously over 200 metres in length. The platform now gives an excellent view of Dunston Staiths and of the river between the King Edward VII and Scotswood Bridges.

Tide Stone, Newburn, NZ 143655. ➤
One and a half miles west of Newburn is the Tide Stone which marks the tidal limit of the River Tyne, nineteen miles from its mouth. The stone bears the three castles of the arms of Newcastle and the date 1783.

Sailors' Bethel, Horatio St., Newcastle. ★
A nonconformist chapel above the East Quayside dedicated to the resident and visiting sailors, built in 1875 to the design of Thomas Oliver, with a later Sunday School room added by Oliver, Leeson and Wood. Of jaunty appearance and recently restored it now acts as offices and accommodation for meetings.

The Quay Walls, Newcastle, NZ 255639. ★
The quay wall stretching from the Swing Bridge to the East Quayside area is listed. It is built of granite with round edged blocks about one metre deep forming the top of the granite wall. A collection of mid nineteenth century bollards are spaced along the quayside.

Trinity House, Broad Chare, Newcastle. ➤
Trinity House was the home of the Master Mariners of Newcastle the guild once responsible for the lighthouses and buoys guarding the approaches to the river, and for the appointment of all sea and river pilots. The Guild, although older, first occurs as a corporate body in 1505. Trinity House itself contains a chapel, hall and ranges of almshouses dating from the sixteenth to the mid-nineteenth century.

Keelmen's Hospital, City Road. ★
Built in 1701 of brick with a central frontispiece with octagonal lantern above, the building enclosing a central courtyard. The Hospital provided accommodation for widows and children of deceased keelmen, or for those who were ill or destitute. The money for the Hospital was raised by a levy of 4d (2p) a tide on the keelmen themselves. The building is now used as student accommodation.

MS Turbinia. ★
The Parsons Marine Steam Turbine Limited developed and built the Turbinia which in 1897 demonstrated the propulsion capabilities of the steam turbine at the Spithead Naval Review by reaching speeds of over 34 knots. This success led to the rapid adoption of the marine steam turbine engine by the Royal Navy for its battleships and by shipbuilders for passenger liners. Only ten years later the " Mauretania ", then the largest liner ever built, steamed out of the Tyne powered by steam turbines. The Turbinia which measures only approximately 30m. is preserved and displayed by the Tyne and Wear Museums Service.

North Tyneside

Life Brigade Watch House, Victoria Crescent, Cullercoats. ★

A watch house built for the Cullercoats Life Brigade designed by Frank West Rich, architect of amongst other things, Ouseburn School, Turnbull's Warehouse, Bolbec Hall and St. Gabriel's Church, Heaton. The Cullercoats Brigade was formed shortly after its Tynemouth equivalent in 1864. The Watch House was constructed between 1877 and 1879. It is now used as a club.

Life Boat House, John Street, Cullercoats. ★

Now used as a garage, an inscribed scroll reading LIFE BRIGADE HOUSE 1867 marks the original use of this building which stands on the west side of John Street above Cullercoats Bay.

Northumberland Dock, Howden, NZ 338662.

Now unrecognisable but once the first enclosed dock to be opened on the Tyne. Opened in the 1850s it covered 55 acres and was the terminal for the important group of colliery railways which brought millions of tons of coal from pits at Cramlington, Seaton Delaval and other mines of South East Northumberland. The dock is now filled in and the area reused.

Albert Edward Dock, North Shields, NZ 353669. ★

The Albert Edward Dock was opened in 1884 to act as a multi-purpose dock but principally to serve the coal trade. Now the centre of a new development, some listed structures survive, notably the lock walls and gates and the hydraulic accumulator tower, all the work of Messrs. Ure and Messent for the Tyne Improvement Commissioners in 1882.

Graving Dock, Liddell Street, North Shields. ★

The only protected graving dock on the Tyne. This early nineteenth century dock is thought to be the oldest surviving example on the river. It measures 65 metres in length and 20 metres in width.

The Old and New High and Low Lights, North Shields, NZ 363684, NZ 360685. ★

Two sets of guiding lights for the entrance to the river. The first pair - the Old High and Low Lights date from 1727. The Low Light was incorporated into a warehouse and recently restored by the Tyne & Wear Building Preservation Trust. The second pair were constructed in 1808 and first lit in 1810. the prominent white towers of these structures are still easily identifiable standing within and above North Shield's fish quay.

The New High Light above North Shields Fish Quay.

Stagline Building, Howard Street, North Shields. ★

The former Tynemouth Literary and Philosophical Society Subscription Library built in 1807. The Society Library merged with that of the Mechanic's Institute in 1869 and the collection was moved to the building further up Howard Street and the old Library became the headquarters of the Stagline Shipping Company. The Stagline emblem is still clearly visible on the gable of the building facing the river. The shipping line continued to trade until 1983.

St. Mary's Lighthouse, Whitley Bay, NZ 353755. ➤

Built on a tidal island called "Bait Island", a 126ft tall lighthouse erected in 1897/8. A chapel occupied the site in medieval times and burned a light in its sanctuary as a warning to mariners. Although the chapel was dedicated to St. Helen, all guiding lights for sailors are "in the care of" St. Mary. The present light ceased to function in 1984 and the structure is now part of the island visitor centre.

St. Mary's Lighthouse

Volunteer Life Brigade Watch House, Pier Road, Tynemouth. ➤

The headquarters and watch house of the brigade stands overlooking the river mouth. The brigade, founded in 1864 was the first in the country. The watch house, in its striking blue livery, dates from 1886 and is still in use for its original purpose. It also contains a small museum to the life and achievements of the brigade.

North Pier, Tynemouth, NZ 378692. ➤

Begun in 1854 the construction of the pier encountered numerous difficulties and was overseen by various engineers including W. A. Brookes, J. F. Ure and P. J. Messent. It was badly damaged and breached in 1897 and much of the 900 ft long pier was rebuilt, a process which was not completed until 1910. A painted rendered ashlar lighthouse with glass lantern stands at the end of the pier.

South Tyneside

Tyne Dock, Jarrow, NZ 353653. ★

Opened in 1859 giving 50 acres of dock mainly to serve the coal trade but also having a timber pond, a grain warehouse and other facilities. At its zenith in one year 7 million tons of coal were shipped from its four staiths with their 42 spouts. Coal shipments ceased in 1967 and the staiths were demolished. A daunting but impressive series of arches brought the rail approach over the South Shields road into the dock but was demolished c1980.

Souter Point Lighthouse, Marsden , NZ 408642. ➤

Opened in 1871 and probably the first British lighthouse to be designed specifically for electrical illumination. The lantern is housed at the top of a 75ft (22.8m.) high stone tower of simple elegant proportions. The original carbon arc lamps were replaced by oil lamps in 1915 but electricity was reintroduced in 1952. Dwellings for an engineer and four keepers, together with an engine house, boiler house and workshops survive from the original plan of 1871 although the original equipment has gone. The lighthouse is located on Lizard Point but was given the name of the nearby Souter Point to avoid confusion with the Lizard Point light in Cornwall.

Life Boat, South Shields, NZ 371676. ➤

The life boat " Tyne ", built in 1833, is preserved as a monument to the building of the boat itself and to the life saving achievements of the people of the town. It sits beneath a cast-iron columned canopy with decorated spandrels. The adjacent clock tower of 1890 has life boat scene reliefs.

Lawe Beacons, South Shields, NZ366680. ➤

Two obelisks, each having a base of stone with brick above but with stone cap erected in 1832 as high and low navigation marks complementing the lights of North Shields.

South Pier and South Groyne, South Shields, NZ 378683. ➤

The Pier was constructed in the period from 1854 to 1895, the South Groyne between the years 1861 and 1867. The Groyne was original built as a straight line but by the 1880s the Tyne Improvement Commission were constructing the southern wave trap at its western end to prevent the silting up of the river.

Volunteer Life Brigade Watch House, South Pier, South Shields. ★

Only three brigades survive: two, the ones in Tynemouth and South Shields, continue in their original watch houses. The watch house was built in 1867 and extended in 1875. The building is wood framed with timber cladding with an octagonal look out tower.

Mill Dam, South Shields, NZ 359669. ➤

The Mill dam area contains two significant river related buildings in the 1860s Former Mercantile Marine Offices, built as a Customs Office just before South Shields was declared a separate customs port in 1865; and the River Police Offices of 1886.

Shipyards, Tyne and Wear.

Little survives of the shipbuilding industry along the banks of the Tyne and Wear. The rapidly changing nature of those areas makes it difficult to point to any historic remnants of the industry. At the time of writing for example it is possible to identify elements of the former Hawthorn Leslie Yard at Hebburn, the adjacent former Robert Stephenson & Company Yard and the dry docks of the disused Brigham and Cowan Yard at South Shields. The picture changes so rapidly, however, that one hesitates to say more.

The South Groyne Light.   *(photograph by P. Jubb)*

W A R E H O U S E S

THE FORMER CWS WAREHOUSE, QUAYSIDE, NEWCASTLE, NZ 256641. ★

This is probably the oldest surviving large scale ferro-concrete building in the country. It was constructed between 1897 and 1900 by T. G. Guerrite of L. G. Mouchel's firm for the Cooperative Wholesale Society (F. E. L. Harris of CWS, architect) using the Hennebique concrete system. The building was built on a ferro-concrete raft in places up to 6ft thick due to the marshy silt ground conditions. The ferro-concrete raft achieved the uniform spreading of the load and was calculated to resist the reaction of the ground at the rate of 2.5 tons per square foot. All the external and internal columns, floors, walls and roof were also constructed in ferro-concrete. In all the building had eight floors with a loading of 6 cwt. per square foot. A further storey with a barrel vault roof was added in 1901. The building is now listed as an early example of this type of construction.

CWS Warehouse, Quayside, Newcastle upon Tyne.   *(photograph by G.B.D.Tullin)*

Newcastle

Broad Chare, Newcastle. ★
A series of nineteenth century brick built warehouses survive on the western side of Broad Chare, some of which have been converted to public houses and theatre use; others are seemingly disused.

Former Warehouse, 35 The Close, Newcastle. ★
Once known as Dove's Warehouse and now a restaurant and public house, 35 The Close is the only example of a late sixteenth century merchant's house with its own wharf remaining on the Close.

Hanover Street, Newcastle. ★
A splendid range of early nineteenth century bonded warehouses built in the 1840s for Amos Spoor and now listed buildings.

Milk Market, Newcastle. ★
A series of large warehouse buildings were built from Broad Chare to the Milk Market from the beginning of the nineteenth century, some of which were particularly fine. Most have been demolished but a recent conversion to residential accommodation has secured the future of what was the most impressive example which has a long 13 bay, seven storey frontage on to the Milk Market, dating from 1830 and later.

Turnbull's Warehouse, Queen's Lane, Newcastle. ★
An impressive and attractive red brick warehouse built in 1888 and 1897/8 for Robinson and Co. printers; to the design of Frank West Rich, architect of the Ouseburn School, Jesmond Dene Real Tennis Courts and the Bath Lane Printing Works, all of which have similar architectural styles.

Former Brady and Martin Building, Northumberland Road, Newcastle. ★
A former office and warehouse built from 1890 to 1897 by W. L. Newcombe for Brady and Martin, wholesale chemical manufacturers; now part of the University of Northumbria.

9, Stepney Lane, Newcastle. ★
Warehouse and offices built in c.1854 for Carver & Co, carriers, and later used as a corn mill. Wedged uncomfortably between the railway and the adjacent towering telecommunications building it has been disused for many years.

Blandford House, West Blandford Street, Newcastle. ➤
A huge impressive warehouse built for the Cooperative Wholesale Society in 1899 by Oliver and Leeson and now used as headquarters for the Tyne & Wear Joint Museums Service and as the County Record Office. Intricate detailing to the outside is reflected in the interior by not only a prestigious board room but also splendid tiled toilet facilities.

South east corner of Blandford House.

ROADS & ROAD TRANSPORT

"INDUSTRIAL" ROUTES AND EARLY TURNPIKES

The origins of many of the County's principal roads lay in the transportation of the goods and materials which dominated its industrial development. Examples of roads which overlay former coal carrying waggonway routes can be found in Newcastle in the form of Black Lane, near Westerhope, and in Gateshead District in the form of Coalway Lane leading toward the River Tyne from and through Whickham. In Southwick in Sunderland some present day roads have their origins in routes for carrying lime to the River Wear. Similarly Salter's Road in the Gosforth and Kenton area takes its name from the salt trade and the Lead Road in the Ryton and Chopwell area from the lead carrying route from the North Pennines. In the same way many street names point to the sites of former industries, Lime Street in the Lower Ouseburn being an interesting example. Taking its present day name from the site of a nineteenth century limekiln, earlier references call the route Coaly Way from an obvious and older industrial connection. Nearby the Glasshouse Bridge also testifies to the former location of the historic centre of Newcastle's glass making industry. Throughout the County names such as Limekiln Road, Gluehouse Lane, Copperas Lane, Tilesheds Lane, innumerable Station Roads, Terraces and Streets, and Pottery Banks are all indicative of seldom surviving industrial activity.

The gradual realisation in the eighteenth century that the condition of, and the lack of care for, the rudimentary regional and national road system was a huge hindrance to the development of trade and thereby wealth (a factor which had been instrumental in the formulation of the coal waggonway) led to the introduction of turnpike trusts. The trusts were formed to " manage " defined stretches of road laid down within Acts of Parliament, to levy tolls at points along the route and thereby pay for the care, maintenance and improvement of the surface, and at the same time reap a tidy profit for the Trustees. In Gateshead, for example, the first road to become a " turnpike " was the Durham and Tyne Bridge Turnpike of 1746 which in reality was little more than the old carriage road through Birtley, Wrekenton and Gateshead to the Tyne, which survives in part today as the " Old Durham Road ". Indeed many of the early turnpikes followed older routes but new routes were planned and executed in time. In the 1820s for example the Durham and Tyne Bridge Trust created the route which in later years formed the A1 through Low Eighton and Low Fell. There were obviously many routes converging on the urban centre of the region and on the river crossings and many of the roads which now sweep into the County from the surrounding districts were eighteenth and nineteenth century turnpikes. Today the heavy emphasis on the road system (to the detriment of the equally historic and important rail network) brings with it a seemingly endless series of alterations, realignments and improvements which in the urban setting leave few vestiges of these early developments.

Gateshead

Milestone, Bensham Bank / Lobley Hill Road, Gateshead. ➤

A prism shaped sandstone milestone, possibly late eighteenth century, for the Lobley Hill and Burnstones Turnpike. It indicates 22 miles to W(olsingham).

Newcastle

County Bridge Stone, B1318, Gosforth. ➤
South of the Three Mile Inn a County Bridge Stone simply carrying the letter C.

Milestone, Hexham Road, Walbottle. ➤
A square sandstone milestone with rounded top, dating from c.1780 with 5 marked on the south side and 53 on the north and a coat of arms on the west face.

Milestone, B1318, North Gosforth. ➤
A cast iron milestone indicating 5 miles to Newcastle and 9 and three-quarters to Morpeth dating from the turn of the nineteenth century but with later alterations.

Tramway Route, Gosforth Park, NZ 243714 to NZ 258713. ➤
Whilst horse racing continues in Gosforth Park the tram service which once brought people in their thousands to race days has long since disappeared. The tramway and the Gosforth Park terminus were owned by the Tyneside Tramways and Tramroads Company until 1930. The tramway penetrated the park and the line is still distinguishable. Some bases of tram posts can be found in the undergrowth.

Tramways Offices and Power Station, Melbourne Street. ★
Former Corporation Tramways Offices and Power Station built in 1901 to the design of Benjamin Simpson. The development from the horse drawn tram to the electric tram had a major effect on the transport system of the area, not least in pushing the NER into the electrification of the Tynemouth railway line and in changing the street scene of substantial parts of Newcastle, Gateshead and Sunderland. This impressive survival is symbolic of the enterprise with which this transformation was undertaken. The former generator hall has a splendid doorway with a lettered arch above. The tramway offices have stained glass over the entrance depicting early tramcars.

Arched entrance to Melbourne Street Tramway Power Station.

Bus Depot, Portland Terrace, Sandyford. ★
A fine bus garage built in 1930 in painted concrete, with a splendid frontage of Greek Doric columns, forming a six vehicle entrance. Now a listed building.

Road Surface, Hanover Street. ➤
One of the Citys few surviving " cobbled " streets. More accurately the surface is made up of " setts " or small cut blocks of red granite, with an inset granite strip on one side to assist carts on the steep uphill climb.

Stables, St. Thomas Street & Percy Street, Newcastle. ➤
Tramway and Brewery stable yards survive in close proximity within the precinct of the University of Newcastle upon Tyne and nearby St. Thomas St. The latter is now restored and is a centre for starter business units and workshops.

North Tyneside

Church Bank, Wallsend. ➤
A late eighteenth century sandstone milestone approximately a half-metre in height with the figure 6 marked on it.

Milestones, Whitley Road, Longbenton. ➤
A series of milestones along the old Coast Road marking the miles from Newcastle to Tynemouth.

South Tyneside

The Tyne Pedestrian and Cycle Tunnels, NZ 328662 to NZ 329658. ➤
The Tyne Tunnel was authorised by Act of Parliament in 1946 to provide a crossing of the river some six miles downstream of the town of Newcastle. Initially two small tunnels were constructed, of 10ft 6in. and 12ft. 0in diameter for pedestrians and cyclists respectively. They were completed in 1951. The approach escalators with 85 ft (25.9m) vertical fall were the longest continuous escalators in the world at the time and the first to permit use by cyclists.

The Tyne Road Tunnel, NZ 331663 to NZ 329658. ★
Further Acts of Parliament authorised the vehicle tunnel, the work being undertaken from 1961 to 1967. The tunnel is 5400ft in length with a 24ft wide roadway in the 31ft 3in diameter bore. The tunnel is lined with cast iron segments and reaches a maximum depth of 80ft below Ordnance Datum. The designers were Mott, Hay and Anderson; the contractor for the earlier tunnel was Charles Brand and Son Limited and for the later work Edward Nutall, Sons and Company Limited.

STREET FURNITURE

THE SEWER GAS LAMPS OF NORTH TYNESIDE. ➤

A series of ten sewer gas lamps, properly called Patent Sewer Gas Destructors, survive in various locations in Whitley Bay and Monkseaton, three of which are listed structures. They are all the product of the Webb Lamp Company Ltd of Birmingham, although some bear the address of their London offices. The sewer gas lamp was invented by Joseph Webb in 1894 and was marketed to local authorities and County Councils throughout the Country. These examples probably date from the first decade of the twentieth century. Webb, himself, died in 1936 but the firm continued in business into the 1940s. In the Whitley Bay and Monkseaton area there are examples of the lamps in Deneholm, Zetland Drive, The Promenade, The Links, St. George's Crescent, Brantwood Avenue, Grange Park, Park Road, The Gardens and Pykerley Road.

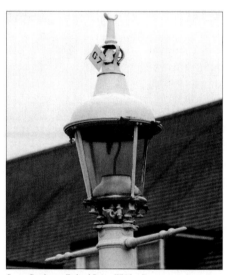

Sewer Gas Lamp, Zetland Drive, Whitley Bay.

Other Gas Lamps within Tyne & Wear

The Green, Ryton, Gateshead. ➤
A series of four fluted cast iron nineteenth century gas lamp posts stand on the North side of the Green in the vicinity of Holy Cross Church.

Garden Lane, Cleadon, South Tyneside. ➤
Another listed nineteenth century cast iron gas lamp post. Here the column tapers from a moulded base and is topped by a square lantern supported on scroll brackets.

A696 at Woolsington, Newcastle. ➤
Two gas lamps survive at the entrance to South Drive, one of which bears the name of Smith, Patterson & Co. Ltd of Blaydon. The standards are fluted and made of cast iron and date from the mid nineteenth century.

Grey Street and Hood Street, Newcastle. ➤
Outside the former premises of Mawson, Swan and Morgan, now Waterstone's, stand ten lamp standards (six on Grey St. and four on Hood St.) dating from 1902-4 by W.H. Knowles and T.R. Milburn. Constructed as gas lamps in cast iron with tapering hexagonal fluted shafts, the lights have now been converted - appropriately outside Swan's former building - to electricity.

Telephone Kiosks

Whitley Bay's K4 telephone kiosk.

Whitley Bay Railway Station Approach, North Tyneside. ➤

Thought by many to be an important part of the functional and decorative fabric of British streets, the red telephone box is becoming a rare sight. Two of the most prestigious designs known as the K2 and K5 models were by Giles Gilbert Scott who also designed, among other things, Battersea Power Station and Liverpool Cathedral. In front of Whitley Bay Station stands the even rarer K4, which design incorporated not only a telephone kiosk but also a letter posting box and stamp selling machine and is now one of only a very small number surviving in the country.

Post Boxes

Chester Crescent, Newcastle. ➤

Examples of pillar boxes illustrating the varying minor modifications and the changing monarchs can be found particularly in the residential areas of the County which developed from the 1870s onwards. Notable amongst these is the box at the junction of Chester Crescent and Sandyford Road in Newcastle which dates from, and bears the motif from, the short reign of Edward the Eighth.

Osborne Avenue, Jesmond, Newcastle. ➤

Newcastle's only hexagonal " Penfold " pillar box, erected in the period from 1872-79. The type, which is one of the earliest, was named after the designer , Mr. J. W. Penfold, and was introduced in 1866. In 1879 the more familiar cylindrical shape was adopted, or more accurately readopted, as the earliest boxes introduced by the novelist Anthony Trollope, who was also a Post Office Surveyor's Clerk, were also cylindrical.

Penfold pillar box,Osborne Avenue.

COAL & COKE INDUSTRY

SEATON BURN, NORTH TYNESIDE.

Brenkley Colliery Incline and Workshops, NZ 223743 to NZ 238739. ★

Brenkley Drift was the last producing element of a long worked site. Seaton Burn Colliery was started in 1844 and worked via shafts and later drifts until the driving of Brenkley Drift by the National Coal Board. The drift, which started production in 1955, was isolated from the original colliery site and the two were connected by an inclined railway. The route of the line fell steeply from Seaton Burn, under the main A1 trunk road from Newcastle to Morpeth and down to the drift mouth. From there a trackway continued down the slope to an upcast shaft, winder house and fan house.

The Workshops were built in two phases with the South East facing stone built single storey block being the earlier. The workshops contained the stores, blacksmiths', plumbers', fitters' and joiners' shop and contained a number of fire places and an internal tubway and probably dated from the sinking of the colliery. The rear extension to the building dated from the period 1899-1922, as did the majority of the buildings which formed the colliery site until the late 1980s. The workshops were restored as units by the Tyne & Wear Building Preservation Trust in 1991.

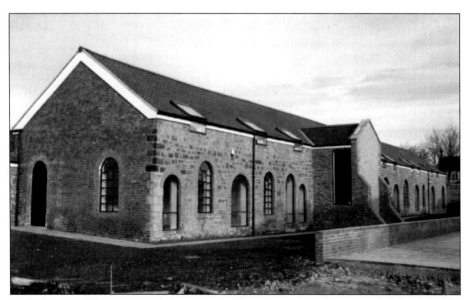

Brenkley Workshops, 1992.   *(photograph by P. Jubb)*

Gateshead

Blaydon Burn, NZ 174633. ➤
Whereas in the late eighteenth and nineteenth centuries water power was at the centre of the industrial development of Blaydon Burn, in the early part of the twentieth century the coal and coke industry dominated the area. A set of coke ovens was built alongside the waggonway which passed through the valley. They would appear to have been built in one long battery and remains of their coking platform can still be seen. The ovens had gone by 1936, superseded by the more modern Priestman Ottovale Coke and Tar Works, built by German engineers. This was the first works in the world to produce petrol from coal. The product was known as Blaydon Benzole and later became National Benzole. The works closed c.1970 and the land has since been reclaimed. The entrance to a service tunnel survives within the valley. Coal mining was concentrated on the Mary and Betsy Pits of Blaydon Burn Colliery which worked until the 1950s. The course of the colliery waggonway can be followed and a number of walls and building shells relating to the screening and loading of the coal lurk under the vegetation.

Dunston Staiths, Dunston. NZ 233652. ★
Dunston Staiths were built by the North Eastern Railway in two stages; the first staith with three berths was opened in 1893. A second similar staith was opened in 1903 immediately to the south and a basin dug out of the riverbank to service it, This set of staiths was taken down to the top of the piles in the 1970s and was further dismantled in the 1980s. However, the majority of the structure survives intact and restored. The staiths are constructed of generally 13" x 13" pitch pine, jointed with bolts and straps. The structure is in three parts; a substructure of piles driven into the mud on

which are superimposed brestles, braced in both directions creating 98 frames at approximately 5.3m. centres and above this run double thickness longitudinal timbers supporting a deck and track beams. The deck slopes at a gradient of 1 in 85 down toward the landward, the track layout along with some drops survive in places. The staiths were the last working timber staiths on the Tyne.

Friar's Goose Pumping Station, Felling, NZ 274362. ➤
The fragmentary remains of a beam pumping engine house on the site of a series of engines built to drain the Tyne Coal Basin. Massively constructed beam-wall survives showing the location of a beam pivot socket, gantry joist holes and a round headed opening; the pivot wall is buttressed. The engine house, as it appeared in c1840 is illustrated in " View of the Collieries of Northumberland and Durham" by the contemporary artist T. H. Hair.

PUMPING ENGINE, FRIAR'S GOOSE, NEWCASTLE.

Friars Goose Pumping Station as illustrated by Thomas Hair.

Derwenthaugh Staiths, NZ 203634.
The Derwenthaugh Marina incorporates the remains of what was the eastern range of Derwenthaugh Staiths which are now part of a jetty. This had been an important coal handling and shipping point since the mid eighteenth century. These remains are part of some nineteenth century staiths used by the Consett Iron Company who opened the colliery at Chopwell and transported coal along the Garesfield and Chopwell Railway. The staiths were taken over by the National Coal Board in 1947 and went out of use in 1960 having served the collieries and coke ovens at Chopwell, Garesfield, Clockburn Drift (Marley Hill) and the Derwenthaugh Coke Works which themselves closed down in 1985.

Coal Drops, Maiden's Walk, Gateshead. ★
A set of eleven coal " chutes " built around 1840 which served to load coal from the elevated terminus and yard of the Brandling Junction Railway to an inclined tubway running to the nearby riverbank. The structure is of coursed squared sandstone built to form bays over which the rail track ran. Stout timber purlins at four levels support timber chutes which guided the coal into waiting waggons below. The drops survive in a substantially complete form and are " listed ".

Whinfield Coke Ovens, NZ 152581. ➤
The scheduled remains of what were the last working beehive coke ovens in the country. Durham beehive kilns were the first successful system of making coke with Durham coal and these ones, built in 1861, worked until 1958. From the range of 193 on the site, five plus two halves have been preserved and a plaque recording their small place in history has been incorporated into the monument. Scheduled as an ancient monument in 1975 the ovens are now held freehold by the Tyne & Wear Industrial Monuments Trust who organised the restoration of the ovens in the 1980s.

Newcastle

Dewley Pits, Callerton. ➤
The Walbottle Moors area was the location of the late eighteenth and early nineteenth century Dewley pits, notable for their connections with the early working life of George Stephenson and as the workplace of his father. Stephenson spent his formative years in the area, gaining his first employment removing cattle from and closing gates on the Walbottle Moors waggonway, before joining his father and brother working at Dewley Burn Colliery. He then worked at Black Callerton Colliery as a brakesman before returning to Dewley Colliery as assistant fireman. Surface contusions can be detected marking the sites of some of these early mining sites, e.g. NZ 168691.

Main Dike Stone, Aidan Walk, Gosforth, ➤
A marker stone of sandstone ashlar inscribed " MAIN DIKE distance from Pit 349 yards, Cut 3 June 1828 " noting the importance of the Main or Ninety Fathom Dike in the development of the Great North Coalfield.

Lemington Staiths, Lemington, NZ 184644.
Lemington was at the highest point on the North side of the Tyne suitable for staiths and consequently early on became an important point for coal handling, and for the convergence of waggonways. There were staiths here by 1640 and the main waggonways which served the eighteenth century staiths can still be traced, notably, Holywell Reins (1767) Walbottle Moors (1781) , Wylam (1748) and Throckley (1751). The last to remain in use were the Wylam Staiths and the fragmentary timber structures which survive are probably their remains. The river improvements of the mid nineteenth century by-passed the staiths but access to them and dredging of the river bed was continued whilst the staiths remained in use.

Throckley Isabella Coke Ovens, Newburn, NZ 153660. ➤

The remains of a set of beehive coke ovens situated within the Newburn Riverside Park. The ovens were built by the Throckley Coal Company which was formed in 1867, principally by Messrs. Stephenson, firebrick manufacturers, and Messrs. Spencer, Newburn Steel manufacturers. The sinking of the Isabella Colliery began in 1867 and the construction of the coke ovens in 1869. Twenty two ovens were built at a cost of £260, the embankment and necessary retaining walls for the attendant railway line costing a further £132. In 1875 a further 22 were constructed and in 1878 a disintegrator for crushing the coal was installed. In 1890 a further 20 ovens were added. Not surprisingly the ovens were constructed using bricks from Stephenson's brickworks and the main market for the coke was Spencer's Newburn Steel Works. Beehive ovens fell out of favour in the twentieth century when by-product ovens allowed the collection of the lucrative gases and by-products which were lost in the older style oven. The Throckley ovens are now fragmentary remains and are being constantly reduced by intrusive vegetation and vandalism.

Burt Hall, Northumberland Road, Newcastle. ★

Until the early 1990s this was the headquarters of the once powerful Northumberland Branch of the National Union of Mineworkers. Named after Thomas Burt the pitman parliamentarian, and leader of the Northumberland miners for 27 years the building features a statue by Canavan (q.v.). The building was constructed in 1895 for the Northumberland Miners' Association

Scotswood Delaval Colliery Incline, Scotswood Road, Newcastle. ★

Part of the inclined railway from the Scotswood Delaval Drift passes under the former Scotswood, Newburn and Wylam Railway in the form of a tunnel passing through the embankment of the Railway across the road from the Vickers' Works.

Town Moor, Newcastle. ➤

An area of possible bell pits can be seen between Ponteland Road and the dual carriageway road to Cowgate (NZ 230660) and an infilled shaft can be identified on the Little Moor (NZ 247673) reflecting the mining of coal which took place in the Town Moor area from at least the seventeenth century.

Neville Hall, Westgate Road, Newcastle. ★

Neville Hall was the headquarters of the North of England Institute of Mining and Mechanical Engineering. The Institute held a comprehensive collection of eighteenth and nineteenth century plans, maps and documents on the northern coal trade and industry, notably those of John Buddle the renowned colliery viewer and mining engineer, which are now predominantly available at the Northumberland Record Office.

Blucher Colliery, Walbottle, NZ 177661. ➤

An engine house, boiler house, workshop and baths building survived on this former colliery site well after the closure of the mine. The original colliery was either sunk or renamed in 1815 when two mines were named in honour of the victorious generals of Waterloo - Wellington and Blucher. The early Blucher mine closed in 1867 but was reopened by the Throckley Coal Company in 1900, from which time the engine house and boiler house date. The pit closed in 1924/25 and reopened in 1938 but final closure came in 1956. Adjacent to the colliery site runs the route of the North Walbottle Colliery Waggonway which served this mine as well as the North Walbottle Coronation Pit.

North Tyneside

Miners' Welfare Hall, B1322, Backworth. ★
The Miners' Welfare Hall in Backworth was situated in an eighteenth century house, dated 1778 to the design of William Newton for R. W Grey and known as Backworth Hall. Listed for its architectural value the use of the building marks what was once an important centre of coal mining activity in the North Tyneside area.

Fenwick Pit, East Holywell, NZ 312730. ★
A number of colliery buildings from the Fenwick Pit of the former Backworth Group of Collieries survive on the road from Earsdon to Backworth. The mine, which closed in 1973 dated from the early expansion of the South East Northumberland coalfield having been opened in 1828. The surviving workshops are, however, much later.

South Tyneside

St. Hilda's Engine House, South Shields, NZ 362668. ★
Brick-built with stone dressing this engine house immediately adjacent to the St. Hilda Shaft, was probably a pumping engine house and dates from the turn of the century. A small modern winding engine house stands nearby but otherwise the rest of the colliery site which closed in 1940 has been cleared.

Westoe Colliery, South Shields, NZ 372668 to 359670. ★
Westoe Colliery was begun in 1909 as a man-riding shaft for the nearby St. Hilda's Colliery. It became a producing mine when the old colliery closed in 1940. A major reconstruction scheme commenced in 1957. The early 1960s

tall enclosed winding tower of the Crown Shaft dominates the site. An unusual but sadly lost feature of the mine was the electrically operated railway which connected the colliery with staiths at Harton adjacent to Mill Dam. The railway had been installed by the original German owned Harton Coal Company.

St. Hilda's Colliery Engine House.

Sunderland

Pit Head baths, Elemore Colliery, Easington Lane, NZ 356457. ★
One of the surviving examples of a series of pit head baths buildings designed by F. G. Frizell in the 1930s. One of the earliest references to pit head baths was in April 1855 when Cramlington Colliery owners were reported to have opened " warm baths and showers at the colliery for their men. " However, pit head baths are more of a twentieth century phenomenon, a large number of baths being built after the Mines Industry Act of 1926 and the setting up of the Miners' Welfare Committee. Elemore is typical of the Frizell designed baths, built completely of brick with a dominant display of chimney and water tank.

Now a listed building and reused as a small engineering works.

Colliery Workshops, Philadelphia Lane, Philadelphia, Houghton le Spring. ★

An impressive group of listed colliery workshops and offices built c. 1882 for the Lambton Colliery Company, all brick built, some with stone dressings, with Welsh slate roofs. The different workshops included an underground battery locomotive shop, winding and cable repair shop, machine shop and surface locomotive shop, a coal-face machinery and electrical overhaul shop and an office block.

Pit Heap, Silksworth Colliery, NZ 374538. ★

The former colliery pit heap has been incorporated into an artificial ski slope forming part of a sports and leisure complex.

Springwell Colliery, Springwell, NZ 286589. ➤

Colliery and railway workshops dating from the opening of the mine and the laying of the first stretches of the Bowes Railway in the 1820s. The stone built engineering shops and other buildings form two courtyard areas. The present day waggon shop was formerly a coal storage building forming part of the coal handling and screening arrangements of the colliery. All now part of the Bowes Railway Scheduled Ancient Monument and in the care of the Bowes Railway Company.

Wearmouth Colliery, Sunderland, NZ 393580. ★

Sunk from 1826 to 1834 to a depth of 1578ft Wearmouth was one of the pioneering deep mines which penetrated the magnesian limestone strata of the area. It was probably the last mine to have a single-cylinder vertical winding engine installed (1868). Steam was used at the mine until the 1950s. A number of reconstructions have altered the appearance of the site but there are currently two brick built winding engine houses surviving on the surface, although they now contain electric winders and have been much altered.

Washington ' F ' Pit, Washington, NZ 302575. ➤

A horizontal twin cylinder steam colliery winding engine built by the Grange Iron Company in 1888 set within its original brick built engine house. The attendant steel lattice headstock survives within the site although the rest of the colliery has been cleared. The site which is now a small museum represents the last vestige of mining in the Washington area. The origins of this site lay in the opening out of various coal measures in the 1770s, the first coal being drawn from this mine in 1778. A number of closures and modernisation schemes took place at the colliery until final closure came on 21st June 1968. The museum was initially opened by the Washington Development Corporation in 1976 but is now in the hands of the Tyne and Wear Museums Service.

Washington 'F' pit headstock with the former cage guides, 1990.

QUARRYING AND LIME BURNING

THE LIMEKILNS OF SOUTH TYNESIDE

Downhill Farm Limekiln, West Boldon, NZ 348604 ★
A three arched kiln of limestone rubble dating from the late eighteenth or early nineteenth century set into a steep escarpment, being more typical of the small kilns producing lime for agricultural purposes than any of the other surviving kilns in the County.

Limekilns convert limestone (calcium carbonate) to burnt or quick lime (calcium oxide). This is achieved by burning the stone with coal at a ratio of about four tons of limestone to one of coal. A fire was lit in the base of the kiln pot and then coal and limestone were alternately charged at the top. Burnt lime was withdrawn through the eyes within the draw arches at the base of the pot, and more charge added at the top. The process was therefore almost continuous. The burnt lime produced in the kilns had many uses. Limestone is still used in the chemical industry, steel making and in road construction, whilst lime is used in building and agriculture. Lime was particularly important to farmers who used it to improve soil conditions. Quicklime was spread on the fields and gradually turned to slaked lime. This helped to neutralise acid soils and aided the release of phosphates, so providing a rich food for the farmer's crops. Nowadays limestone is crushed for many purposes, rather than burnt. However, in their heyday limekilns were highly important to the region's economy. As well as large industrial batteries like Marsden, there were hundreds of small kilns throughout the area similar to the one at Downhill Farm.

Marsden Limekilns, Marsden, NZ 404644. ★
A bank of industrial limekilns thought to have been built in the 1870s and set in the magnesian limestone coastal outcrop. Limestone for the kilns came from Marsden Quarries which had been at work since the early years of the nineteenth century. Coal to burn the limestone came from Whitburn Colliery which was opened out in 1874. Both the kilns and the colliery closed in the 1960s but stone is still worked in the nearby quarry. There are a number of differences between the various types of kilns on the site, but there are basically two types of structure. The earlier type consists of seven complete kilns within a long stone battery. The later kilns, built of brick, stand at the south western end of the stone battery. These are circular and wrapped around with iron bands which prevented the kilns from collapsing through expansion of the hot brickwork. Within the stone range of kilns are fifteen draw arches, each arch having two or three " eyes ". Of the two brick built kilns one has three arches with a single " eye " in each, and the other has a solitary draw arch with three " eyes. " In front of these stands the remains of a brick and concrete platform dating from the 1950s from which the lime was loaded into trucks on the railway which ran below. The railway was originally built as a colliery line in the 1870s by the Harton Coal Company, but was extensively rebuilt when the present coast road was built in 1926.

Marsden Limekilns, South Tyneside.

Sunderland

Springwell Quarry, Springwell, NZ 284587.
★

The world famous " Newcastle Grindstones " in fact came from Gateshead being produced from quarries like this one, the last one now working. This very tough fine grained sandstone occurs in a 36.5m bed and has also been used for pulpstones and as a building stone.

Monkwearmouth Limekilns, Sunderland, NZ 390582. ★

An enormous bank of disused lime kilns with some 25 draw and access arches, mainly blocked along a 328 ft (100m.) frontage, the kilns themselves being largely filled in. In blocks of varying construction (sandstone, magnesian limestone and brick) and period,

one block near the west end carries an 1872 keystone, while the large block at the east end carries an 1821 keystone. A chute can be seen which passes through the block from above, perhaps for delivering ready burned lime, or limestone arriving at the kilns from Fulwell. At the west end are two, possibly three kilns with a curved front wall.

Fulwell Limekilns and Quarries, Sunderland, NZ 392597. ➤

A complex of kilns constructed in magnesian limestone to burn the same stone extracted from extensive quarries behind. The kiln structure is now within the Mill Garage site. Much of the quarried area with its unique " cannonball " formation has been reclaimed but formerly the routes of three nineteenth century waggonways for lime carriage to the Wear could be followed.

POTTERY AND CLAY

MALING'S FORD (B) POTTERY, WALKER ROAD, NEWCASTLE, NZ 270641. ★

Maling Pottery was, in its time, world famous. By the close of the nineteenth century the Company had become one of the largest producers of ceramics in the country. Their products were wide ranging but their stock-in-trade for many years was the production of pots and jars for jam and marmalade companies. As well as these mundane goods, however, Maling's manufactured a variety of intricate and beautifully patterned goods, including commemorative ware for coronations and other national celebrations.

The firm was started by William Maling in 1762 on the north bank of the River Wear at Hylton. The family had come to England as Huguenot refugees in the seventeenth century and settled near Scarborough. William Maling moved to Sunderland in the 1720s and later set up the pottery as a business interest for his two sons, Christopher Thompson Maling and John Maling. The North Hylton Pot Works was run by the family until John Maling's son, Robert transferred the whole business to a site in the Ouseburn in 1815. For Robert Maling to move away from Sunderland at a time when the Wearside pottery industry was booming, was bold and adventurous, but his business acumen was greatly rewarded as the Company went from strength to strength in the Ouseburn. The Ouseburn Bridge Pottery, set up by Robert Maling, was superseded in 1859 by a large newly built and heavily mechanised works on Ford Street, called the " Ford Pottery ". The new works were established by Robert Maling's son, Christopher who then sold the old Ouseburn Bridge site to Bell Brothers who reopened the premises as the " Albion Pottery ". The new factory was able to produce more in a week than the older works had done in a year. With a production capacity of up to three quarters of a million items a month Christopher Maling amassed a huge fortune.

In 1878 a second, even larger, plant was opened up half a mile to the east. Known as " Ford B Pottery ", it was thought to be the largest pottery in the country and could produce a million and a half items per month. With the two works working together the company was employing over a thousand people at the turn of the century. The original works on Ford Street continued to produce jam and marmalade pots, whilst the Ford B Works concentrated on new markets, such as sanitary ware. The firm flourished in this period but before the twentieth century was very old, a number of factors began to effect the prosperity of the company, not least of which were the death of Christopher Maling and the increasing use of glass, rather than earthenware, for storage jars - particularly for jam.

When the miners' dispute of 1926 starved the kilns of coal for many months, the old Ford Street site closed for production and never reopened. The buildings were cleared out and sold in the following year. The Ford B Works struggled on through to the Second World War and beyond. In

1947 the whole Company was sold to Hoults Estates Ltd. The name " C. T. Maling & Sons " was retained and under the guidance of Frederick Hoult the firm staged a post-war recovery, only to be undermined by competition from overseas in the 1950s and early 1960s.

C. T. Maling & Sons closed in 1963. The Ford B Works was given over to furniture storage. Today, it is better known as " Hoult's Yard ". Ford Street survives in the Lower Ouseburn Valley, but only a few fragments of buildings testify to the site of the former Maling's Ford A Pottery.

The former Maling Ford (B) Pottery, now Hoults Yard.

Gateshead

Cowen's Brickworks, Blaydon Burn, NZ 180635 & NZ 166623. ★

Cowen's had brickworks at either end of the Blaydon Burn valley. Brickworks were established here in the eighteenth century and fireclay is thought to have been mined here even earlier. The High and Low Works were of considerable size. Little remains now of the lower works but some buildings survive from the upper works. Blaydon Burn House, where Sir Joseph Cowen lived prior to moving to Stella Hall also survives.

Lilley Brickworks, A694, Rowlands Gill. ★

An office building from the former Lilley Brickworks stands on the A694 in Rowlands Gill, a plaque identifying its previous existence upon its wall. The site of the works has been reclaimed. Commencing c1883 with the building of brickworks and coke ovens at the mouth of the Lilley Drift Mine, by the 1950s it was producing 150,000 bricks per week but closed in 1976.

South Tyneside

Brick Kilns, Tilesheds Farm, Boldon, NZ 366622.

A pair of horizontal through draught kilns surviving on a site otherwise cleared of its former buildings and now host to a piggery. Three mid-nineteenth century brick making sites were situated within a quarter of a mile radius in this area. The surviving kilns, recorded in 1994, are due for demolition.

THE GLASS INDUSTRY

THE OUSEBURN GLASSWORKS, NEWCASTLE.

For centuries the manufacture of glass was the second most important industrial activity on Tyneside. Newcastle was for some time the national centre of bulk glass-making. This important position was established at the beginning of the seventeenth century when glass factories or " glasshouses " as they were known, were set up near the mouth of the Ouseburn, east of Newcastle. Prior to this time the making of glass had been carried out in the more heavily wooded areas of the South of England. However, concern about the dwindling timber resources of the country as a result of the use of wood in early industrial processes led manufacturers to move to coal mining areas in search of fuel for their ventures. In the early years of the seventeenth century both the manufacture of glass with wood fuel and the importation of glass from overseas were prohibited by Royal Proclamation; at the same time a monopoly was granted to Sir Robert Mansell, the Treasurer of the Navy and later Vice Admiral of England, for glass production using " sea cole ". Mansell set up three glasshouses to the east of the mouth of the Ouseburn and is thought to have encouraged Huguenot families to take employment in his works. The glass produced in his works was said to be cloudy and of poor quality but Mansell's monopoly lasted until the beginning of the Civil War, after which glassworks spread along the banks of the Tyne,

many owned by Huguenot families such as Henzell and Tyzack. In " An Impartial History of the Town and County of Newcastle upon Tyne " published in 1801 the Rev. John Baillie says that " glass is the richest branch of trade at Newcastle next to coal. " Between 1772 and 1812 the number of glasshouses on Tyneside increased from 16 to 30 and their locations ranged from Lemington to South Shields. The industry continued to prosper until the second half of the nineteenth century when decline set in and many works including the huge complexes at the Ouseburn closed down. The buildings have been lost, many disappearing with the quayside extensions of the first decade of the twentieth century.

St. Lawrence bottleworks under demolition 1908

Gateshead

Shipley Art Gallery, Prince Consort Road, Gateshead.
A fine array of local decorative glassware forms part of the museum's collections and displays.

Newcastle

Lemington Glassworks, NZ 184646. ★
Lemington Glassworks was commenced in 1787 by a partnership who had obtained a ground lease from the Duke of Northumberland to set up "The Northumberland Glass Company." The location was ideal for river transport and for local coal supplies but sand, alkali and suitable clay for melting pots had to be brought in by sea and river. Initially flat glass was the main product and soon four large glass cones had been erected. The works had a variety of owners throughout the nineteenth century but in 1906 the site was purchased from the Duke of Northumberland by G. E. C. who pursued a programme of expansion and mechanisation for the production of bulbs and tubing for all types of electric lamps. Eventually this programme led to the demolition of all but one of the cones which survives on the site to this day. As one of only four extant cones in the country, this is a highly important industrial monument. The cone which stands in the region of 120 ft. high was cleaned, repaired and repointed in 1993 as part of a laudable programme financed by the owners and English Heritage with the help of Newcastle City Council.

Lemington Glass Cone at the turn of the Century

South Tyneside

Chimney Remains, Former Cookson's Glassworks, Mill Dam, South Shields. ★
On the site of former workshops of Harton coal staiths are the remains of a chimney carrying a datestone of 1865. The structure is c.30 ft high, and 10ft by 10ft on plan. Built of brick with a fire brick lining, the chimney has a stone string course at about 15ft from the ground. On the west and south faces are markings from former abutting buildings. The chimney has been truncated. Internally it is 5ft by 5ft in plan and features flues within the walls about 7ft and 10ft from the ground. Until 1989, it was enclosed within British Coal workshops but on their demolition it was revealed as the only surviving element of the former Cookson's Glass Works.

Cookson's interest in this site began in the eighteenth century when John Cookson, son of Isaac Cookson, expanded the family's interests from its base in the iron and steel industry. Cookson's ownership of the site continued until the 1840s when the works passed to R. W. Swinburne & Co. Swinburne manufactured glass here until 1876. In 1865 James Swinburne took over as manager and instigated a number of changes based upon a new complex of buildings of which this chimney formed a part. The ownership of the site changed in the late 1870s to the Tyne Glass Company whose name disappeared from local directories in 1892 which probably indicates the last working year of the glassworks.

Harton Chimney Mill Dam, South Shields.

Sunderland

Sunderland Glass Trail. ➤
The recently devised Glass Trail is designed to give visitors a flavour of Sunderland's importance as a centre of glassmaking. It incorporates fine collections, the manufacturers and other sites of interest such as the historic stained glass of St. Peter's Church.

Hartley, Wood & Company Glassworks, Portobello Lane, Monkwearmouth. ★
Situated in Portobello Lane, Monkwearmouth, the works were opened in 1893 by James Hartley, the grandson of the founder of the Wear Glass Works of Trimdon Street, Sunderland. Hartley was joined in this Company by Alfred Wood, a specialist in the making of coloured glass who had moved a few years earlier from Birmingham to the Wear Glass Works. Wood became sole owner of the Portobello Works in 1908, but kept the original name of the Company. The firm continue to specialise in producing stained and coloured glass which is supplied principally to churches and public buildings. The Battle of Britain window in Westminster Abbey was produced by this Company - the House of Commons, Coventry Cathedral and St. Paul's also have examples of Hartley, Wood craftsmanship. Of particular interest are the methods used at the works where both cylinder glass - a sixteenth century technique - and crown glass - a late eighteenth century technique - are made.

Corning Ltd. Glassworks. ★
The American firm of Corning were the pioneers of heat resistant glassware, commencing development of " borosilicate " products in 1915. Its production in this country started in 1922 when the Sunderland firm of James A. Jobling acquired the sole rights to its manufacture in the British Empire. Both Corning and Jobling marketed their goods under the name of " Pyrex ". Joblings closed down production of ordinary glass in the 1960s and concentrated their manufacture on the " Pyrex " range. Corning gained a 40% share in Joblings in the 1950s and took over completely in the 1970s and continued to produce heat resistant glass.

IRON & STEEL INDUSTRY

FORMER CROWLEY IRONWORKS, WINLATON MILL, NZ 186605. ★

A hugely important industrial archaeological site which for many years has been undervalued, largely because of extensive modern reuse and lack of archaeological activity on the site. The iron works was founded in 1691 by Ambrose Crowley. The large majority of the complex was erected between the late 1690s and 1718, with limited later alterations and additions. The complex consisted of a forge, slitting mill, plating (rolling) mill, steel furnaces, nail and file-makers workshops, warehouses, offices and housing. The Crowley Company also operated a similar complex at Swalwell, together with extensive workshops at Winlaton village. The Crowley works employed up to a 1,000 people and had their own laws and social security system.

The complex in its early days was unique in Europe. It was the forerunner of the factory system and also formed the basis of the North East's tradition of ironworking and naval engineering. The site worked until the mid/late nineteenth century and was later overlaid by coal waste from the nearby Clockburn Drift (part of Marley Hill Colliery) and by Derwenthaugh Cokeworks. Recent excavation (1992) has shown some survival beneath the coal waste and has exposed a considerable element of an eighteenth century dam with associated spillway and race.

Winlaton Mill Dam, 1993.

Gateshead

Dam, Blaydon Burn, NZ 178634. ➤
A substantially intact horseshoe dam which formed part of a water-powered forge site within Blaydon Burn. Excavated in 1982 much of the detail of the structure has been recorded and a certain amount of consolidation work undertaken. Vegetation has however once more taken a hold. The dam structure lies in part over an earlier straight dam which shows up on the First Edition Ordnance Survey map. The style of the stonework suggests that the dam is late eighteenth century and was possibly part of a corn mill until the early nineteenth century when the forge came into operation. The buildings and waterwheels were last used in the 1890s as a foundry by the Blaydon Company of Smith Patterson. This is an impressive surviving feature which deserves attention.

Former Smithy, Smithy Lane, Lamesley. ★
Now converted to form rooms for the adjacent public house and hotel the early nineteenth century single storey smithy building retains a number of internal features, principally two hearths.

Forge, Hood Square, Winlaton. ★
A late eighteenth century sandstone rubble forge building with pantiled roof with stone slates at the eaves, being one of the few surviving examples of the many works and shops which were once active in Winlaton village - a listed building.

Forge, Pennyfine Road, Whickham. ★
Late eighteenth/early nineteenth century listed forge built in sandstone rubble with some internal features surviving, notably a central wooden plank panel in a stone block floor and a forge and anvil.

Newcastle

Brown's Buildings, Ponteland Road, Kenton Bank Foot. ★
The dilapidated remains of a smithy which was formerly part of the early nineteenth century group of buildings at the bank foot. Some details can still be discerned including the iron tyre ring inlaid into the smithy floor. A site unlikely to survive future development.

Tyne Iron Works, Lemington, NZ 186645. ★
The Tyne Iron Works were founded in 1797 and by 1801 had two blast furnaces with a Boulton and Watt Blowing Engine. The works were closed in 1876 and dismantled in 1890 and the site was subsequently bisected by a main road. To the North of the road are coke oven and calciner remains. Between the road and the river was the main site with prominent but unidentified arches which may have housed puddling or re-heat furnaces or may simply represent a viaduct ramp to blast furnace top. Another prominent ramp nearby incorporates a number of curious rooms. At the riverside stands the former manager's house and office dating from the 1830s.

Spencer's Steel Works, Walbottle Road, Newburn. ★
John Spencer began the Newburn complex by purchasing a former flour mill for use in grinding files in 1822. The works concentrated in the production of springs for the new and burgeoning railway industry, so much so that by 1851 Spencers won the only award for the manufacture of springs at the Great Exhibition. The firm reached its zenith at the turn of the century, covering 60 acres and employing approximately 1800 people. The firm diversified into steel plate for the shipbuilding industry and in 1904 manufactured the plate for the " Mauretania ". The decline in the

shipbuilding industry in the 1920s however, brought the collapse of the firm. In 1928 John Spencer and Sons was founded to work the site and concentrated on the production of railway springs and axles, altering this policy only during the Second World War when production was turned to gun springs and barrels. The 1960s brought the closure of the firm resulting from falling demand. A range of partially reused nineteenth century buildings survive on the original site in Walbottle Dene, whilst on the later larger site between Lemington Road and the river, one major building from the steelworks has been reused.

North Tyneside

The Links, nr Watts Road, Whitley Bay. ➤ Large areas of the sea front have been mined for ironstone since the eighteenth century. The Northumberland County History refers to the working of waste heaps of older coal pits on Whitley Links for ironstone. The Rev. Hodgson, writing in 1821, referred to rubbish heaps of old coal pits, " in them massive pieces of ironstone in flattened spheres." Many workings were filled in when the Interceptor sewer was constructed in the 1970s.

An illustration of the Tyne Iron Works with a cone of the Lemington Glassworks in the background, probably early nineteenth century.

THE LEAD INDUSTRY

THE ELSWICK LEAD WORKS, NEWCASTLE, NZ 243642. ★

For an area which had been pre-eminent in the lead trade for centuries the North East was relatively late to establish lead manufactories. Apart from some eighteenth century colour works which may have used lead products, the first lead works was not set up in this region until 1778.

Elswick Lead Works was set up by Samuel Walker, an ironfounder from Rotherham, Richard Fishwick and Archer Ward, both from Hull, as " Walkers, Fishwick & Co. " in 1778. By 1779 the works were producing white lead and by the mid 1780s the concern was generating £ 3,000 annual profit and a 30% increase in turnover while diversifying into red lead, lead rolling and, by 1797, lead shot. The Elswick shot tower was one of the earliest to be built, being in operation by 1797. At 174ft high and with a drop of 150ft it was a notable feature of the area. In 1825 Mackenzie described it as a " most striking and remarkable object ... It is a circular brick building, with a stone cupola, terminated by a chimney and is ascended by a winding staircase in the interior. This singular edifice presents itself to travellers about two miles north of Chester le Street and never fails to excite their curiosity. " Mackenzie also repeated a story to the effect that shortly after its completion the tower was found to be " alarmingly out of perpendicular " but that this was corrected by the simple expedient of digging away the earth from its more elevated side

Engraving of Elswick Lead Works showing the shot tower (left) and the surviving office buildings (right).

until it recovered its perpendicularity. Shot production ceased in 1951 and although the tower was soon after listed it returned to its old habit of listing and had to be demolished in 1968/69.

The Elswick Lead Works underwent a number of changes of name in the years after its inception being known as " Walkers, Parker & Co. " from about 1802. It has been claimed that the original concern was the earliest founding firm in what became known as " Associated Lead Manufacturers " and is now known as " Cooksons ". The present name also harks back to an early Tyneside company founded in 1704 but not entering lead manufacture until 1851. In 1924 the Cookson lead concern initiated the merger with Walkers, Parker to form ALM and since that time has expanded considerably mainly through new acquisitions. By 1980 lead's contribution to the

firm's profits was a mere 10% for by then most of the firm's products had no connection with lead at all. However, lead is re-cycled at Elswick and the Cookson Group Headquarters is still in the eighteenth century houses and offices of Walkers , Fishwick & Co.

Newcastle

Northumberland Lead Works, Lime Street, Newcastle. ➤
Within the City Farm complex is a surviving masonry structure which contains a relocated plaque reading " Northumberland Lead Works 1871 ". The Lower Ouseburn valley had been the site of two considerable nineteenth century lead works.

Northumberland Lead Works plaque within the grounds of the Byker City Farm.

ROPE : WALKS & WORKS

ROPERY BANKS, EAST QUAYSIDE, NEWCASTLE, NZ 263643. ★

The manufacture of rope, principally for the shipping industry, has existed on both Tyneside and Wearside for centuries. Long rope-walks where, prior to the mechanisation of the industry at the beginning of the nineteenth century, strands of rope were laid out and plaited, can be seen on the earliest plans of both Newcastle and Sunderland. Corbridge's plan of Newcastle (1722) marks two roperies beyond the town walls, one at St. Ann's and one at the Shield Field. Similarly Raine's Eye Plan of Sunderland features the unmistakable " goalposts " which signify the early rope-walk. The steeply sloping Ropery Banks indicates the site of the former St. Ann's Ropery of Joseph Crawhall, whose family lived in the recently demolished (1993) St. Ann's House, adjacent to the former Miller's Hill.

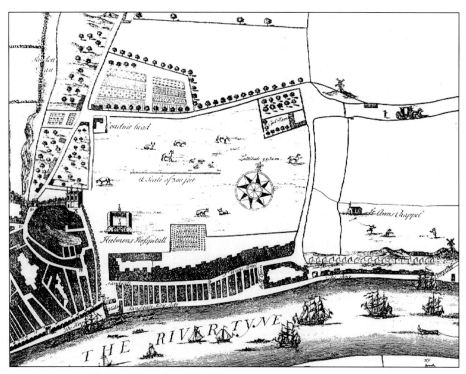

Extract from James Corbridge's plan of Newcastle upon Tyne 1722

Newcastle

St. Lawrence Wire Rope Works, St. Lawrence Road, Newcastle. ★

A former rope works building interesting not only as a vestige of the rope industry on Tyneside but also for the use of ferro-concrete in the early twentieth century extension to the building. A 376 ft long building was added to the site for Messrs. T & W Smith Ltd, the roof of which comprises 33 ferro-concrete trusses.

North Tyneside

Willington Rope Works, Willington, North Tyneside, NZ 316666. ★

The history of rope-making at Willington goes back to the eighteenth century. A factory was established by the tidal Willington Burn in 1789 by Chapman who invented a machine for rope manufacturing without a rope walk. Following a severe fire the complex was rebuilt in 1873. Ownership of the works passed to Haggie Brothers of Gateshead in the nineteenth century. The firm was taken over by British Ropes and continues to trade as Bridon Ropes manufacturing heavy industrial wire ropes including those for the Bowes Railway rope-worked inclines.

Sunderland

Webster's Ropery, Ropery Road, Deptford, Sunderland, NZ 385578. ★

Although the history of this building is obscure it is almost certainly the oldest factory building in Sunderland. According to Surtees (History of Durham, c.1812) and later G. Garbutt (History of Sunderland, 1819) the firm of Grimshaw Webster and Company opened a ropeworks at Deptford in 1797 in a four storey building of 100ft by 30ft, and the present structure appears to be of approximately this date. It is shown on a plan of property at Deptford dated 1801 held within Sunderland Library which also holds illustrated documents relating to the Fothergill Process, patented in 1793, which was used at the works. Thus it is believed to be the world's first Patent Ropeworks, i.e. not having a rope walk. The building, which is now listed has been modified and converted to create a pub / restaurant.

The former Webster's Ropery, 1994.

WIND & WATER MILLS

FULWELL WINDMILL, SUNDERLAND, NZ 392595. ➤

This is the most complete windmill in the region and currently in process of restoration by Tyne and Wear Industrial Monuments Trust. Built in 1821 on the site of a previous mill, it remained in use until 1949 although it had lost its sails long before then. A gas engine installed c1900 powered the stones until closure. Some external restoration was undertaken by Sunderland Corporation in the 1950's. Since the early 1980s the Trust has stabilised the structure, reintroduced the floor levels and staircasing, reopened some blocked openings, installed new doors and windows, renewed the timber sail framework and reconstructed a non-operational fantail. As well as general decoration and display of some milling equipment a series of interpretation boards have been supplied for the benefit of visitors to the mill which is opened by the Trust on an occasional basis. The base of the mill is cylindrical, the large diameter set into sloping ground. The base occupies two floors and it supports a tapering 4-storey tower of smaller diameter so that the base also forms a reefing stage. The cap is hemispherical; its framing supports an iron windshaft with wooden brake wheel, iron cross-end and 4 sails. The base and tower, both of attractively weathered magnesian limestone are a special possibly unique feature being an extension of the podium design at Cleadon (q.v.). Internally the first floor contains a dressing machine and a small alcove office with fireplace. The second floor houses the underdrives to two pairs of millstones with a 3 ball governor operating on both pairs of stones together with a free standing belt driven pearl barley machine. The third floor has 2 pairs of millstones, the fourth is empty and fifth gives access to the cap. The striking and fantail gears are missing.

Fulwell Windmill showing the restored fantail and sail frames in 1993.

Gateshead

Path Head Mill, Blaydon Burn, NZ 174632. ➤

This site contains the earliest built features of industrial archaeological interest within Blaydon Burn for the mill was probably pre-nineteenth century. The remains of this water driven corn mill are fragmentary but parts of the leat as well as low walls remain in the undergrowth. A later brick and concrete overflow channel can be traced from the former mill dam to the site.

Leap Mill, Burnopfield, NZ 175572. ➤

A water corn mill site although marked as a Naptha Manufactory on the first edition Ordnance Survey map. The present buildings are a two and a half storey mill with an adjoining one and a half storey house, all stone built with slated roof. There is also an adjacent pigsty with henhouse over and a tail race beneath, a detached byre and stable with hayloft. A good dressed stone dam is immediately to the rear of the mill and this presumably powered an overshot waterwheel. The tail race is entirely in a tunnel about 15 metres in length. The milling equipment is substantially intact and is of standard form with two pairs of stones, a sack hoist and a drive which was probably to a low kiln; the crown wheel is entirely wooden. Other earthworks perhaps relate to the naptha manufactory. The mill has been preserved and renovated and is open to the public on a regular basis. Technically in County Durham, but the stream forms the County boundary and there are no other water mills open to the public in the area.

Moormill Farm, Greenford Lane, Lamesley. ★

Moor Mill was advertised as a mill fitted with three pairs of French and one pair of blue stones

in the Newcastle Courant of 26th October 1754. The site was also mentioned by the eighteenth century Swedish industrial voyeur, Angerstein in the same year. The mill no longer survives but elements of the race can be followed along field boundaries and road sides near the extant farm.

Whickham Mill, Chase Park, NZ 210610. ➤

There are a number of early references to Whickham mill but its later history is not known. A mill is mentioned in the receiver's roll of 1307. Similarly it is referred to in documentation in 1567. Local lore has it that when the Scots invaded Northumberland and Durham in 1640 at harvest time, crops were destroyed, the people fled and the upper millstones were broken or buried by order. The existing tower would seem to date from a later structure. The dates on the door lintels are not to be trusted.

Whickham Windmill Tower.

Windmill Hills, Gateshead, NZ 252631. ➤

Windmill Hills was, along with Bensham fields and parts of Low Fell, one of the areas of medieval common land of Gateshead. From the Middle Ages Gateshead was one of the main centres of milling in County Durham. Mackenzie, in his " History of Durham " published in 1834 wrote that Windmill Hills was " studded with corn mills which, seen at a distance, impart a lively and picturesque effect to the landscape." Richardson's mid nineteenth century engraving of the area shows ten mills. Plans of the same period show nine mills in the area, seven of which were actually on Windmill Hills. In style these were windmills of the post-mill variety, having timber bodies and sails set upon brick or stone roundhouses. The Gateshead Observer reported in September 1859 that many of the mills had been dismantled and existed as merely round houses, some of which were later turned into dwellings. All Gateshead's mills were closed by 1890 and a report in the Evening Chronicle in 1927 marks the demolition of the last of the old windmills on Windmill Hills.

Newcastle

Heaton Windmill, Armstrong Park, Newcastle, NZ 267658. ➤

Possibly early eighteenth century tower mill recorded on a View of Newcastle in 1743 and marked as such on a 1746 map of the town. An advertisement in the Newcastle Courant in July 1760 gives the tenant as one Jonathon Hutchison and advertises it to be let. In 1800 the ownership is shown as Mathew White Ridley but by 1844 it is shown as " in ruins ". Ordnance Survey 1st Edition (1856-64) marks it as an "Old Mill". The standing tower therefore represents a building which has been disused for perhaps 150 years.

Chimney Mill and Mill House, Claremont Road, Newcastle, NZ 240656. ★

The site of a windmill since pre 1649 the last mill built on this location was erected in 1782. It was the first five sailed mill in the country and was built for the purpose of " manufacturing of wheat into flour for the London and any other markets ". The five sails were carried on an iron axis. This was a smock mill and was designed by the famous engineer, Smeaton. It was perhaps the last mill to work in Newcastle. It was out of use in the early 1890's. The sails were finally dismantled in the 1920's and the windshaft and cap recoved in 1951.

Ouseburn Mills. ➤

The Ouseburn had considerable strategic importance as an area of early industrial development. The burn could support water-powered industries whilst being tidal at its junction with the Tyne, just to the East of the city walls. It is a complex area and many sites of interest lie near the burn as it stretches about 2 miles inland from the Tyne. Jesmond Old Mill (formerly Heaton Corn Mill) NZ 258671, served as a flint mill for a few years but only the shell of the mill, some gearing and foundations of an adjacent cottage, inhabited at least to 1911, survive. The external overshot wheel is to be rebuilt. The head race can only be followed with difficulty, back to and through the bridge at NZ 254675. The tail race led directly into the headrace to Deep Dene Flint Mill at NZ 257672 along the line of the present footpath, from which the race diverges as Deep Dene approached. Little remains of the original mill. Its tailrace discharged to the burn, but one of the several weirs hereabouts took water off along a clearly defined headrace parallel to the present footpath which terminates in a sluice gear in the rear wall of a former millpond, now the garden to Millfield House, (NZ 262663). The site is complicated by extensive landscape gardening but was formerly known as Busy

Cottage, having a cornmill and also a forge owned by Rayne & Burn. Elements of the nineteenth century Jesmond Vale Flint Mill were recently exposed and recorded. Walls and floors of some ancillary buildings were found but the main part of the mill has disappeared.

South Tyneside

Boldon Colliery Water Corn Mill. NZ 344627. ➤
Little survives of the mill other than earthworks but the long headrace shows as an earth embankment winding along the valley being taken into a large diameter iron pipe at a point where a railway embankment was taken across it in 1844. Elements of the site were excavated and consolidated in 1993 by South Tyneside Groundwork Trust. An on-site interpretation plaque was erected as part of the Trust's work.

Cleadon Windmill, NZ 389632. ➤
In Bishop Hatfield's fourteenth century survey it was recorded that the bond tenants of " Whitburne and Clevedon " held the tenancy of a windmill. The location of this medieval mill is not known but it is commonly the case that such sites are continually re-used.

The last Cleadon Mill is thought to have been built in the early 1820s. Local verbal tradition states that it was built for the Reverend George Cooper Abbs of Abbs House and Cleadon Hall in Cleadon Village. Abbs (1798-1878) was a notable scholar, naturalist and friend of many of Tyneside's nineteenth century luminaries. Certainly a Cleadon Mill was in operation in 1828 when Parson and White's Directory recorded Joseph Watson as a corn miller at Cleadon Mill. Sixteen years later in 1844 (Vint and Carr's Directory of Cleadon) Thomas Metcalfe had become the miller. However by

the 1850's the mill was being worked by the Gibbon family who seem to have run the mill until its closure sometime in the latter half of the nineteenth century. The mill is marked, and presumably in use, on the First Edition Ordnance Survey Map c1860. When the mill closed is not known but no miller is recorded in Kelly's Directory of 1879, although the same family were still in residence at Cleadon Hill Farm. Certainly the mill is marked as disused on the 1896 Second Edition Ordnance Survey Map. It was later used as an artillery base during the first World War.

West Boldon Windmill, NZ 355612. ★
The shell only of a short, stone tower mill with slight taper; constructed of magnesian limestone but with sandstone lintels and sills. The door headstone is dated AD1834. It was converted to domestic accommodation in c1984.

Whitburn Mill, NZ 407626. ➤
Comparatively little is known of Whitburn Mill. The present tower originates from c1796 when the previous mill blew down. A "Coasting Pilot" Survey of 1779 marks a post mill on the site. Obviously the fate of the wooden mill encouraged the owner to construct a more substantial tower mill, using stone from the surrounding magnesian limestone quarries.

In 1828 Parson and White's Directory recorded John Storey as a corn miller at Whitburn Mill. The mill is marked on the First Edition Ordnance Survey Map of c1860 as a Corn Mill. Also marked is a path from Mill Lane, bending round the contours of the field and leading to the mill. The mill must have closed at some point in the following decades. No miller is mentioned in Kelly's Directory of 1879 and the mill is marked as disused on the 1896 Ordnance Survey Map. Its last use was in the Second World War when the Observer Corps took it over as a lookout post for hostile aircraft.

Whitburn Mill after an extensive restoration scheme undertaken by South Tyneside Council in 1990/91.   *(photograph by P. Jubb)*

AGRICULTURE

THE URBAN FRINGE

Whilst obviously not as rich and diverse as the neighbouring counties of Northumberland and Durham the urban fringes of Tyne and Wear retain a number of fine agricultural buildings which reflect the nineteenth century advances in farm technology and building. At the heart of the movement which saw the marriage of industry and agriculture was the invention and widespread adoption in this region of the barn threshing machine, which became available in 1786. Around this fulcrum the planned farms of the mid nineteenth century grew. Where new " model " farms were not developed existing farmsteads were adapted to bring farms up to date with the technology and methods of the day. The way in which such farmsteads developed clearly affected both the layout and appearance of the buildings. The new farms were planned on the basis of ideal farm management with purpose built barns, sheds and animal housing constructed in ideal locations within the complex. This approach brought about the typical " E " shaped plan which gave two south facing fold yards where animals could be held and manure collected. Typically in this arrangement the two storey threshing barn incorporating the all important threshing machine would stand to the north of the fold yards, helping to shelter the beasts within the yards, and behind it would be the attached gin-gan or horse wheel house which provided the power for the thresher. From the nineteenth century, stationary steam engines were also in use to drive the thresher and the pleasing often octagonal shape of the wheel house gave way to the small engine house with its attendant chimney. A common variation on this form was the U shaped complex which did not have a central range and so had a single fold yard. However the same drive for production and efficiency which brought about the innovations of the late eighteenth and early to mid nineteenth century has now made the buildings of that time largely superfluous to the needs of modern farming. Added to this threat, the spreading conurbations of the County have either engulfed former farm complexes or have taken so much land out of production that farm owners seek alternative uses for their building ranges.

New Horton Grange, near Dinnington.

Gateshead

Dovecote, Axwell Park House Farm, Gateshead, NZ 189622.
A dovecote dating from the turn of the nineteenth century in the form of a straight sided circular tower built of coursed rubble with a Welsh slate roof. The pigeon nesting boxes still line the interior.

Path Head Farm, Blaydon, NZ 164635. ★
Little remains of either the former settlement or the farmstead of Path Head, but the two storey threshing barn with an adjacent waterwheel pit, which probably housed a breast wheel, is still visible on a site which contained a number of rubble built, pantiled farm buildings

Ice House, A695, near Bradley Hall, Ryton.
An 8 metre entrance passage leads in to the brick and stone walled ice house built into the side of a hill in the late eighteenth century.

Ice House, Gibside Hall, Whickham.
A stone entrance gives access to a brick lined tunnel leading to the hemispherical chamber of this late eighteenth century icehouse.

Nesting boxes, Axwell Dovecote.

Newcastle

New Horton Grange, near Dinnington, NZ 198756. ★
The most impressive example of a planned farm in the County. Kelly's Directory for 1858 describes the house and farm buildings as the most complete and extensive in Northumberland. The farm buildings date from c.1858 - 1863 and were built for Sir Matthew White Ridley. They include fine ranges of sandstone granaries, hemmels, cart shed, stables, turnip house with a dovecot tower rising up to form the visual focal point of the complex. Farm workers' dwellings and a fine farm house all built as part of the planned farm complete this impressive site which continues largely in agricultural use, with the exception of the main farmhouse which is currently a hotel/restaurant.

Gosforth Home Farm, NZ 252695. ★
An example of a farm which although developed in the early to mid nineteenth century underwent further improvements later in the century. Also an example of a farm where the motive power changed from the gin-gan to the steam engine. The surviving imposing set of barns has been converted to housing.

Bullock Steads, Ponteland, NZ 204693. ★
Another converted set of farm buildings and house, but dating from the late eighteenth century and demonstrating the use of brick as the prominent visual material with the use of stone on the more hidden elevations.

Whorlton Grange, near Westerhope, NZ 193679. ★
A planned range of farm buildings designed by John Green for the Duke of Northumberland, erected in the 1850s, now converted to residential use for the elderly. This

was a planned and mechanised farm and the small engine house with its tall square chimney survive. The farm was formed by amalgamation of land and consequently had no farmhouse.

Whorlton Hall Farm, near Westerhope, NZ 186687. ★
Formerly the home farm for Whorlton Hall, the E shaped ranges of the farm have been converted into housing. Prior to this the farm retained its mid nineteenth century appearance and plan form.

Ice House, Gosforth Park, NZ 243715. ➤
A late eighteenth century sandstone and brick ice house with an earth mound over. A stone entrance giving access is blocked by an iron grille.

North Tyneside

Shiremoor House Farm, Middle Engine Lane, North Tyneside, NZ 327697. ★
Sensitively converted to a public house and restaurant many of the original features of the farm survive. The serving area of the bar is within the old wheel house. The mid nineteenth century buildings include a typical arrangement of ranges and fold yards and bear a number of similarities in style to Whorlton Grange, suggesting the work of John Green.

South Tyneside

Downhill Farm, West Boldon, NZ 348605. ★
A virtually complete restored wheel house with machinery attached to a two storey threshing barn. The wheel house roof forms part of the threshing barn roof instead of being a separate structure. This is not a planned farm but an example of one which, like Topsy, just grew.

Ice House, Front Street, Whitburn. ★
An eighteenth century limestone icehouse with an earth mound. A 2 metre long tunnel forms a passage into the domed interior

Sunderland

Ice House, Morton House, Fencehouses.
Another eighteenth century hemispherical brick example with an earth floor and an earth mound over.

And many others ...

Clearly there are a large number of individual buildings and groups of farm buildings in the five Districts of Tyne and Wear which have a considerable history or have points of interest which reflect the developing and changing technological and architectural approaches to farming. Equally clearly there is not the scope here to go into detail on a subject which is of considerable significance and has been only scantily studied.

FOOD AND DRINK

SPILLER'S MILL, ST. LAWRENCE, NEWCASTLE, NZ 270635. ★

Spiller's Tyne Mill was completed in 1938 and was, then, the tallest flour milling building in the world. Spiller's had come to Newcastle from Bridgewater in 1896 when they acquired Davidson's Phoenix Mill in the Close. The Tyne Mill replaced this older complex. There were two main buildings at the Tyne Mill - the Silo and the Flour Mill. The Silo was designed to store 34,000 tons of grain. The mill contained a warehouse, the flour mill and an animal food mill. To serve it the deep water berth was improved and the rail network along the quayside extended. The old Phoenix Mill was seriously damaged by fire during the Second World War.

Spiller's Mill.

Gateshead

Newcastle

Baltic Flour Mill, South Shore Road, Gateshead. ★

Originally consisting of a grain silo capable of holding 200,000 tons, a flour mill and animal food factory, only the silo now stands, Although designed prior to the Second World War it was constructed in 1949. Built for Joseph Rank in a neo-classical monumental style. Internally it contains over one hundred vertical shafts. This cliff like building now plays host to a colony of Kittiwakes.

The Cooperage, Close, Newcastle. ★

No. 32 the Close, built as a house, later used as a cooperage and now a public house and restaurant. The structure dates from the fifteenth century with later alterations, having a sandstone ground floor with timber framed upper floors with rendered infill. Jettied first and second floors are topped with a pantiled roof.

Flour Mill, Lime St., Newcastle. ★

A large flour mill built c1840. Standing next to the John Dobson designed former flax mill, the two form an imposing backdrop to the course of the Lower Ouseburn. The building was later used for storage and is now partly empty and partly used as a workshop.

Brewery Office, Percy St., Newcastle. ★

Built from 1896 to 1900 by Joseph Oswald as offices for Newcastle Breweries Ltd.. A red sandstone ground floor and bright red upper floors give the building a prominent appearance on Percy Street. The pride of the interior was the mahogany panelled boardroom. " Newcastle Breweries Ltd. " can still be seen inscribed above the double-door entrance to the building. Across the road behind the Farmer's Rest public house is a building which is thought to have been a Ginger Beer Works.

Deuchar House, Sandyford Road, Newcastle. ★

Now converted former bonded warehouse and boiler house for Sandyford Brewery, built in c.1840, which still bears the legend " Office 1904 Robert Deuchar Ltd. "

Baltic Flour Mill   *(photograph by G.B.D.Tullin)*

North Tyneside

Ballard's Smoke House, Fish Quay, North Shields. ★
A c.1920 smoke house built originally as a military building in the nineteenth century within the area of the seventeenth century Clifford's Fort. Ventilation is by top hung weatherboarded ventilation shutters and a long louvred ridge ventilator with four tall ventilator stacks.

Old Maltings, Tanner's Bank, North Shields. ★
A late eighteenth/ early nineteenth century sandstone former maltings building, later used as a smoke house in an area where this usage became common.

South Tyneside

Mill Dam Brewery, Mill Dam, South Shields. ★
Behind the Customs House and Police Offices a much modified brewery has survived, of which the three storey brick built maltings block can still be identified.

Sunderland

Old Brewery, Durham Road, Houghton le Spring. ★
This may be a misnomer for this large four storey stone building built c.1874 which occupies a prominent site near the centre of the town. The structure, built of magnesian limestone, may have been a maltings rather than a brewery. Interesting features of the building are internal cast iron columns, segmental brick heads to the window openings and a projecting gabled wooden grain elevator. Although a listed building its size seems to have rendered it a difficult candidate for adaptive reuse and it has consequently led a precarious and ultimately damaging existence over recent years.

Houghton Brewery showing the former grain elevator.

THE WATER INDUSTRY

RYHOPE PUMPING STATION, SUNDERLAND. NZ 405525. ➤

Constructed in 1866-70 for the Sunderland and South Shields Water Company to the design of their consulting engineer Thomas Hawksley, the station closed down in 1967 due to a slight increase in salinity but more importantly because of the Derwent Reservoir coming in supply. The entire station is extant with engines and boilers in their original houses, coal store, workshop, chimney, cooling ponds and reservoir (now covered). A Superintendent's house, complete with former boardroom, and a terrace of three station workers' cottages with stable/coach, were added in 1874. The engine house contains two double-acting, compound rotative beam engines by R & W Hawthorn of Newcastle which were used to raise water in two lifts from deep wells in the magnesian limestone at each end of the beams. The beams are 33 ft (10.1 m) between pump rod centres and each flywheel is 24 ft (7.3 m) diameter. The cylinders are 27 $\frac{1}{2}$ in. dia. by 5 ft 4 in. stroke (H.P) and 45 in. dia. by 8 ft stroke (L.P). The design speed is 10 strokes per minute, pump stroke is 10 ft 8 in. (3.25 m) and delivery was 40,000 gall/hour against a 243 ft (74.1 m) head. Two steam crab winches still exist as well as the hand winches used during the construction of the engine house. The original five Cornish boilers were replaced by three Lancashire boilers in 1908 with a design pressure of 100 psi but the working pressure is 35 psi. Since 1970 Ryhope Pumping Station, which is a Scheduled Ancient Monument, has been in the joint care of the Water Company and 'The Ryhope Engines Trust' and the latter steam the engines for public display on many occasions during the year.

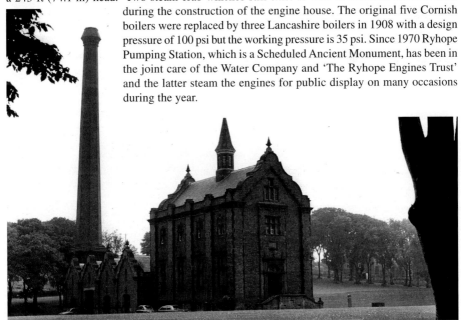

Ryhope Pumping Station

Gateshead

Swan Pond, Carr Hill, NZ 268610. ★
There has been a reservoir at Carr Hill for over
150 years. A plan was brought forward in 1875
to replace the earlier reservoir with a much
larger version. The Carr Hill Service Reservoir
was completed in 1880 to the design of John
Bateman. It has since been replaced by a totally
enclosed reservoir constructed of reinforced
concrete.

**Byermoor Pumping Station, Marley Hill,
NZ 203573.** ★
Small pumping station built in 1912 to pump
sewage from nearby colliery houses. An
unprepossessing brick building but with
original machinery intact. The equipment was
designed by Siemens and installed by Hughes
and Lancaster. The electrically operated
compressors and switchgear are as originally
installed.

Newcastle

**Newburn Water Pumping Station,
NZ 160656.** ★

Constructed in 1855 for the Whittle Dene Water
Company to extract river water, using a
pumping engine of c1832 previously used in
Newcastle for the same purpose. This engine,
probably a modified Cornish type by Robert
Hawthorn and Company, was replaced by two
new Barclay 'grasshopper' engines in 1866
although by 1884 these seem to have been on
standby to supplement the delivery from
Wylam Station. Only the engine house and
boiler house remain, both being stone built with
slated hipped roofs.

Town Moor, Newcastle, NZ 246658. ➤
Water for eighteenth and early nineteenth
century Newcastle was collected in reservoirs
on the Town Moor. By the 1870s these had long
been disused but are recognised today as the
origin of the boating lake in Exhibition Park.

Valve Houses, Hexham Road, Throckley. ★
A former valve house, now a storage building,
constructed in c1870 for Newcastle and
Gateshead Water Company and a later valve
house built c1890 for the same Company stand
on either side of Hexham Road and are listed
buildings. As part of the improvements in
supply of water to the growing town in the
1870s large areas of filter beds were
constructed at Throckley.

Newburn Water Pumping Station

Benwell Pumping Station, NZ 205634. ★
The pumping station was erected in 1857 together with reservoirs at Benwell and Fenham. The engines were supplied by Morrison and Company, being 50 h.p. horizontal cylinder 26" diameter and 6' 0" stroke. These engines were replaced by similar ones in 1868. Two Tangye engines were installed in 1879 and two Tangye triple expansion steam driven units were installed in a new building in 1904. Electrically driven pumps were added in 1924.

Another splendid example by Thomas Hawksley, the ornamental grounds contain a neo-Italianate engine house, boiler house and cottages all dominated by a campanile chimney. Built c1860, originally steam powered with 2 cornish engines and 3 cornish boilers, the station was electrified c1930. The complex forms part of a Conservation Area and the buildings are listed, the splendid chimney carrying the more prestigious 2* status.

Sunderland

Fulwell Water Pumping Station, NZ 389606. ★
Constructed for the Sunderland and South Shields Water Company and in operation by 1856 with two rotative, pumping engines of 70 hp each. These were replaced by two Uniflo engines in 1925 but the station is now electrified. Engine and boiler houses remain, built in brick but with stone dressing to openings, corner buttresses etc.

Humbledon Water Pumping Station, NZ 384554. ★
The earliest surviving pumping station in the area being constructed between 1846 and 1849. Also the most utilitarian of the early Sunderland and South Shields Water Company Stations. Designed for a single cylinder, double-acting non-rotative house engine; the surviving engine house has external buttresses to help support the beam pivot. The station was electrified in 1924.

Stonygate Pumping Station, NZ 345517. ★
Built in 1890 to the design of J E Wolfe, resident engineer for Sunderland and South Shields Water Company. The engine house, pumping station, walls, gates and gate piers are all listed structures.

South Tyneside

Cleadon Water Pumping Station, NZ 389632. ★

Cleadon Water Pumping Station Tower.

ELECTRICITY SUPPLY

TYNESIDE'S EARLY POWER STATIONS

In the decades which straddled the turn of the twentieth century the electricity supply industry advanced from an almost experimental stage to become an established and hugely important element of the industrial structure of Tyneside. Whereas in 1890 Newcastle's first power station was still under construction, by 1910 virtually all the great industrial concerns on the north bank of the river, along with the NER and the Tyneside Tramways and Tramroads Company, were consumers.

Newcastle's first power station was built by The Newcastle Upon Tyne Electric Supply Company (NESCO) in Pandon Dene where advantage could be taken of the railway and its coal supply. It was a small scale venture using a reciprocating steam engine with ropes and pulleys to drive its generators, producing electricity for lighting.

Much of the progress which would occur in the generation and distribution of electricity in the following years was the result of the work of Charles Merz, son of Theodore Merz one of the directors of NESCO, who pioneered the idea of a central power station supplying current for industry on an industrial scale. Together with his colleague William McLellan he designed the Neptune Bank Power Station which opened in 1901 and took over from the Pandon Dene Station. The Neptune Bank station, the engine house of which survives within the Thermal Syndicate Complex on Neptune Bank, was Britain's first supplier of three phase electricity for industry.

Such was the progress in the industry however that even the innovative and successful Neptune Bank station was soon overtaken by the need for a larger supply - principally to power the electrified NER line from Newcastle to Tynemouth - which saw the construction of Carville Power Station. Carville opened in 1903 using the largest turbines in commercial use at the time. It was eventually enlarged and augmented by the building of Carville 'B' in 1916. Once again the engine house of the original station survives. Merz and McLellan became a major consulting engineering firm which retains its Tyneside base to this day.

Gateshead

Newcastle

99 Kells Lane (Underhill), Gateshead. ★
A large house built in the 1860s which was the home of Sir Joseph Swan from 1869 to 1883, where he conducted experiments which led to the development of the filament for the first practical incandescent electric lamp. The house was the first in England to be wired for domestic electric lighting and some early fittings survive.

Lemington Power Station, NZ 186645. ★
The Lemington Power Station was commissioned by the Newcastle and District Electric Lighting Company in 1903. It is a typical brick-built power station building with round hooded openings and ridge ventilators. The station ceased generating in 1919 but continued in use until 1946 as a substation supplying the local tramway.

Joseph Swan Commemoration, Swan House Complex, Pilgrim Street. ➤
In 1969 Joseph Swan's life and inventions were commemorated by an illuminated fountain and a symbolic sculpture " Articulated Opposites" at Swan House in Newcastle City Centre. A glass case affixed to a nearby wall contains a statuette and a copy of the filament lamp which Swan exhibited at the Newcastle Literary and Philosophical Institute in 1879. Near to here is Mosley Street which in 1880 was the first street in the United Kingdom to be lit by electricity.

Manhole Covers and Street Markings. ➤
The streets of Newcastle retain some tell-tale signs of the development of electricity supply in the City. A number of manhole covers are inscribed with the names of the early supply companies. These are particularly prevalent in the City Centre and what were then the more affluent suburbs of the city, consequently most examples come from the streets of Jesmond. Clayton Road, Osborne Avenue and Eskdale Terrace boast numerous examples (fourteen at the last count) of NESCO " Newcastle Upon Tyne Electric Supply Company Ltd. " manhole covers. The instances of covers marked the " Newcastle Electricity Supply Company " are relatively common and always occur in groups of three. Examples are in Acorn Road, Eskdale Terrace and Otterburn Terrace. DISCO covers

Joseph Swan

are to be found in the City Centre there being on the last inspection two each on Percy Street, Newgate Street and Clayton Street. Some kerb stones within these areas also carry strange hieroglyphs, notably various combinations of triangles, arrows, crosses and squares incised into the stone which were coded guides to the early supply lines, indicating such features as joints in cables.

Carliol House, Carliol Square. ★

Completed in 1927 Carliol House was one of Newcastle's finest interwar buildings. Built as the offices of NESCO it featured electrically heated boilers for central heating, high-speed electric lifts and a central vacuum plant for cleaning the building.

Sunderland

Philadelphia Power Station, Voltage Terrace, Philadelphia. ★

Built c.1906 as a power station for the Durham Collieries Power Company in yellow brick with red brick dressings. The station was incorporated into the Newcastle Upon Tyne Electric Supply Company system by 1911. The building has been in more recent years a central garage for the former National Coal Board.

Street Names. ★

The streets of the area in which the former Philadelphia Power Station stands mark the original use of the building, bearing the unusual names of Voltage Terrace and Electric Crescent.

Philadelphia Power Station.

INDUSTRIAL HOUSING

COLLIERY SETTLEMENTS IN GATESHEAD.

The increasing ability to mine deeper reserves of coal, pump increasing amounts of water from shafts, ventilate larger areas of underground workings and furthermore to transport coal greater distances to the region's rivers allowed the development of deep mines throughout the Great Northern Coalfield in the first half of the nineteenth century. The extent of the available coal, and the long-term financial commitment of the venturers were instrumental in the simultaneous growth of mining communities centred on the deep mines of Northumberland and Durham. The pit village took many forms from the single rows forming a square around the mine typified at West Cramlington Colliery, to the serried ranks of terraces which formed the " largest village in the world " at Ashington. Many mining villages grew on the back of former agricultural communities, others were purpose built by mine owners for their workforce. Some villages, more accurately small towns, were an amalgam of colliery company houses and houses built speculatively and rented to the workforce, Hetton le Hole being one such community. Principally however the large coal companies provided colliery houses for the miners employed in their pits. This acted not only as an incentive to those employed to retain their jobs but also as a lever for the employers to impose their will upon a workforce reliant on the coal owner for both wages and homes.

Colliery housing was nevertheless often far superior to either agricultural workers housing or to speculatively built tenements and from the mid-nineteenth century onward some coal companies prided themselves on building model villages and houses. These were villages laid out to allow good light and ventilation to the terraces of houses, to encourage better health and sanitation and to provide either allotments or gardens. The houses themselves were of a higher standard than previously but retained the marked distinctions between those for the surface and face workers and those for the deputies; and beyond that those for the higher pit officials. A typical example is Marley Hill - a model village laid out at the turn of the century containing a traditional grid of terraces with large detached houses for the officials, a board school, church, Miner's Welfare Institute and associated facilities and a row of 1930s Aged Miners Homes. Similarly, although in different surroundings, the village of Clara Vale has retained the form of the colliery village as developed in the years immediately following the sinking of the mine in 1893. Interestingly both of these examples were earmarked for oblivion as Category D villages in the infamous 1951 County Durham Development Plan and are both now Conservation Areas.

Newcastle

minimum size of any inhabitable room (70 sq.ft.).

Dinnington Colliery Village, NZ 232727. ★
The sinking of Dinnington Colliery was started in August 1867. The colliery village was designed to the standards of a model village, but by 1873 only some houses had ashpits and privies. The mine closed in 1960 but a number of terraces of the original village survive.

Sallyport Crescent, Newcastle. ★
The earliest surviving council-built houses in Newcastle having been constructed in 1913-16 under the supervision of Mr. Halford, Property Surveyor to the Corporation. The crescent consists of 44 flats with rear yards enclosed by low walls. Some restoration and revitalisation has been undertaken.

Tyneside Flats, Newcastle. ★
The typical and distinctive Tyneside flats were constructed throughout the area to house the expanding workforce of late nineteenth century Tyneside. Built in long terraced rows they survive in their thousands to this day. The standard plan of two flats, one upstairs, one downstairs was part of the original design which dates to the 1840s. Similarly the internal arrangements of rooms was standardised - the lower flat being entered by a long entrance corridor which led to a large front bedroom, a smaller back bedroom and the living room. Beyond the living room lay the kitchen, and in later years bathrooms were added to the kitchen ends. The back door from the kitchen led to the rear yard which contained the coal house and toilet. The upstairs flat being identical except for the added provision of a small bedroom over the downstairs entrance corridor. The minimum distance between terraces was laid down in 1892 at 40 ft. at the front and 20ft at the rear. The regulations also dictated the minimum width of a frontage (18ft) and the

James St., Westerhope. ★
A street of solid stone built two storey houses notable for being served by a tramway from the nearby colliery bringing coal and also taking away refuse from the houses. This type of system was not uncommon in some of the mining communities of South East Northumberland, particularly in Ashington.

Garth Heads, City Road. ★
Industrial workers dwellings created in 1869 for the Newcastle upon Tyne Improved Industrial Dwellings Co. Ltd. The building was extended in 1878. It is probably the earliest surviving example of philanthropic industrial housing in the city.

Garth Heads   *(photograph by G.B.D.Tullin)*

North Tyneside

Knott Flats, Tynemouth Road, North Shields. ★

An inter-war example of a philanthropic slum clearance scheme, now maintained by the local authority. Sir James Knott was a prominent local shipowner who, at the turn of the century, owned one of the North East's largest merchant ship fleets, the Prince Line.

South Tyneside

Boldon Colliery, NZ 341622. ➤

Boldon retains a number of facets of the mining village, including a Miners' Hall, a number of chapels and a fine semi-circular range of Aged Miners' Homes situated on Hedworth Lane.

Andrew Leslie's Hebburn, NZ 306652. ➤

Andrew Leslie founded his shipyard at Hebburn in 1853 and by 1864 he had built 300 houses for his workers. St. Andrews Presbyterian Church built in 1875 for about

£15,000 was largely financed by Leslie as one of a number of community facilities provided by the yard owner. Leslie's firm merged with R & W Hawthorn in 1886 to form Hawthorn Leslie.

Mariners Cottages, Broughton Road, South Shields. ★

Falling slightly out of the realm of industrial housing but nevertheless a form of housing provided for a section of the local workforce, Mariners Cottages are a range of single storey cottages set out round three sides of a garden courtyard built in 1839 by the Mariners Asylum and Annuity Society which was founded in that year. A further row completing the square was added, to the design of Oliver and Lamb, in 1859-62.

Souter Point Lighthouse Cottages, Mill Lane, Whitburn. ★

A fine range of two storey houses built surrounding a courtyard to provide accommodation for the lighthouse keeper and staff, constructed in 1871 as part of this important site (q.v.). The eastern range of buildings is attached to the lighthouse by a one storey passage.

Souter Point Lighthouse and Cottages.

Sunderland

Joicey Aged Miners' Homes, Philadelphia Lane, Shiney Row. ★

A row of twelve aged miners' cottages built in 1906 for the Durham Aged Miners' Homes Association. Built of yellow brick with bands of red brick and roofs of Welsh slate. Whilst not dissimilar to aged miners' homes throughout the region the added architectural elegance has given this group listed status.

Shiney Row, NZ 334523. ➤

Shiney Row retains a number of interesting housing groups, as well as the aforementioned aged miners' homes, including Chapel Row which features a chapel set at the centre of a terrace, unusual Tyneside flats which have no front doors, only rear entrances, and some early flat roofed houses built for pit deputies.

Sunderland Cottages. ★

Whereas the Tyneside flat became the usual and typical form of workers' housing in and around Newcastle, the Sunderland Cottage became the standard on Wearside. Near to the river and housing principally shipyard workers the cottage was typically a single-storey dwelling with a single , one and a half, or double frontage. The addition of dormer windows allowed the cottages to develop to one and a half storeys, and the addition of front bay windows gave a more gracious appearance and a slightly roomier interior. The style began, like the Tyneside flat, in the 1840s and was built up to the First World War. As well as shipowners both coal owners and glass manufacturers built homes of this type to provide housing for their workforce.

Trafalgar Square, Sunderland. ★

Fourteen almshouses dating from 1840 built for the Trustees of the Muster Roll to house aged merchant seamen and their wives and widows. Designed by William Drysdale and built of brick around three sides of what Pevsner describes as a " ship-shape square ". In the courtyard is a splendid lampholder also dating from c.1840.

Red Hill House, Springwell Lane, Springwell. ★

Large detached former manager's house for the Bowes Railway and Springwell Colliery site built of brick with Welsh slate roof in 1908. The house is listed as a building of architectural or historical interest because of its association with the adjacent Bowes Railway, which is itself a Scheduled Ancient Monument. The house was subdivided by a previous occupant and for some time acted as the offices for the Bowes Railway Company Limited. It has now been brought back into single private ownership.

Red Hill House

STATUES & MEMORIALS

THE HARTLEY COLLIERY DISASTER MEMORIAL, ST. ALBAN'S CHURCHYARD, EARSDON, NORTH TYNESIDE. ➤

Within Earsdon Churchyard is the memorial " erected to the memory of the 204 miners who lost their lives in Hartley Pit, by the fatal catastrophe of the engine beam breaking 16th January 1862". The disaster was instrumental in the passing of legislation requiring mines to have at least two means of escape. Perhaps the most moving and eloquent of the County's memorials, the names and ages of all those lost are recorded, including that of a visitor to the mine who also died in the tragedy. The site of the doomed Hester Pit of Hartley Colliery is marked within the village of New Hartley in Northumberland.

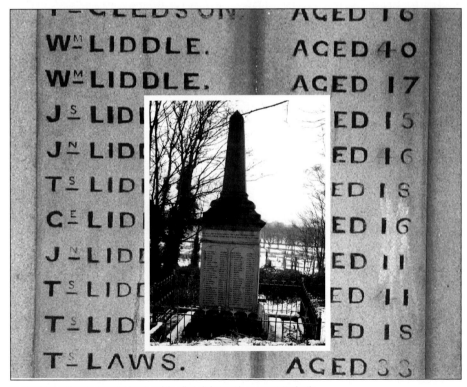

Hartley Colliery Disaster Memorial (inset) and the effect of the tragedy on one mining family.

Gateshead

Newcastle

Memorial to Thomas Ramsay, Blaydon Cemetery. ➤
Erected by the miners of Durham to commemorate the long and self-sacrificing labour in the cause of human progress of Thomas Ramsay who died in 1873.

Tomb of Thomas Hepburn, Church of St. Mary, Felling. ➤
Thomas Hepburn was the founder of the first successful miners' union in the area and his tomb was erected by the miners of Northumberland and Durham on his death in 1864. It is inscribed " SHORTER HOURS AND BETTER EDUCATION FOR MINERS."

Monument to George Hawks, Bensham Road, Gateshead.
Hawks' Iron Works became, at one point, perhaps the most important industrial complex in Gateshead, although George Hawks himself (1801-63) is better known as Gateshead's first Mayor. The monument was erected by " his friends and by the workmen of Gateshead Iron Works, of which he was the fifth senior partner".

Armstrong Memorial, Barras Bridge, Newcastle. ➤
Statue of the mighty Sir William, later Lord, Armstrong and screen walls depicting some of his achievements. Erected in 1905/6 the life-size statue commemorates the founder of the largest nineteenth century engineering, armaments and ship building complex in the region. He was also a considerable benefactor to the City. The left hand screen wall shows guns being lowered onto a ship whilst the right hand screen illustrates Armstrong's Swing Bridge. The statue and relief panels are made of bronze and the surrounding steps, walls, piers and pedestal are of sandstone.

Memorial to Sir William Armstrong.

Statue of a Miner, Burt Hall, Northumberland Road, Newcastle. ★

Canavan's statue, based on Hedley's painting, of a miner in pit gear carrying a pick, which stands aloft the former Northumberland Miners' Association headquarters (q.v.).

Statue of Joseph Cowen, Westgate Road, Newcastle. ➤

Statue erected in 1906 in ashlar and bronze to commemorate the life of Joseph Cowen (1829 -1900) , industrialist, proprietor of the Newcastle Chronicle and Member of Parliament from 1873 to 1886.

Statue of Robert Stephenson, Westgate Road, Newcastle. ➤

Erected in sandstone and bronze in 1862 to the design of J. G. Lough the heroic figure of one of the country's leading engineers is surrounded at each corner of the plinth by figures representing the areas of Stephenson's achievements: miner, locomotive engineer, blacksmith and bridge builder.

Hawthorn Family Tomb, Newburn Churchyard. ➤

Robert Hawthorn died in 1842 having founded an engineering firm on Forth Banks in Newcastle which was to become one of the most important in the region. Hawthorn himself was involved in the early use of steam engines for marine propulsion and was one of the group of influential Newcastle engineers of the early nineteenth century.

William Hedley Tomb, Newburn Churchyard. ➤

William Hedley, who died in 1843, was one of the developers of the earliest locomotives and was responsible for the construction of the " Puffing Billy " which operated on the Wylam Waggonway. Often forgotten in the general enthusiasm for George Stephenson and his position as father of the locomotive.

South Tyneside

Statue of Sir Charles Mark Palmer, Tyne Street, Jarrow. ➤

Charles Mark Palmer was one of Tyneside's leading nineteenth century industrialists who was instrumental in both the expansion of the railways and particularly in the development of Tyneside shipbuilding. In 1852 Palmer's yard built the John Bowes, the first economically viable screw driven steam collier and thereby revolutionised both the coal trade and the face of Tyneside shipbuilding. Palmer's Yard was for many years the lifeblood of Jarrow and its closure in 1932 was a crippling blow to the town. The statue was erected in 1903 and stands aloft a square pedestal with panels illustrating the SS. John Bowes, a coal miner and HMS Resolution.

Sunderland

Elemore Colliery Disaster Memorial, High Street, Easington Lane. ➤

Memorial to the 28 men and boys who perished in the disaster at the Elemore Colliery in 1886. Elemore was one of the group of mines opened by the Hetton Coal Company in the 1820s.

Tomb of Nicholas Wood, Churchyard of St. Nicholas Church, Hetton le Hole. ➤

Friend and mentor of George Stephenson, Nicholas Wood was involved in the development of the locomotive and of some of the early colliery railways .He was also involved in the Hetton Coal Company and in the construction of the Brandling Junction Railway. He died in 1865 aged 70 and his tomb is in the churchyard of St. Nicholas in Hetton le Hole.

M I S C E L L A N Y

Gateshead

Dunston Soap Works, Colliery Road, Dunston. ★

Once part of a series of ferro-concrete structures built for the Cooperative Wholesale Society at Dunston. The complex, which formerly included a flour mill and grain silos, dates from two periods, 1907-8 and 1911-14. The Soap Works brings together the use of the Hennebique ferro-concrete construction system and a modified Renaissance architectural style designed by L. G. Ekins of the CWS. Used for a number of years as a hide and skin works but currently disused.

Dunston Soap Works

Green's Tannery, Bankwell Lane, Gateshead. ★

Now disused but in origin an eighteenth century industrial building used as a tannery, a once flourishing Tyneside industry of which nothing now remains.

Lintzford Paper Mill, Lintzford, Gateshead, NZ 151571. ★

Paper has been made hereabouts since 1695 but the oldest of the present buildings are probably late eighteenth century. Originally water but later steam powered. Paper was manufactured until 1924 after which the site was converted to a printing ink works. The two and three storey stone and brick buildings are now mostly converted to housing.

Pub Names. ➤

The names of many public houses of the region are evocative of the industrial past, Newcastle's Scotswood Road once contained many such examples but is now reduced to the " Hydraulic Crane " in deference to Armstrong's invention. The " Five Wand Mill " in Bensham. relates to the site of a windmill. There are many more...

Newcastle

W. D. & H. O. Wills Tobacco Factory, Coast Road, Newcastle. ★

Former tobacco manufacturing factory built of red brick and Portland Stone in the 1940s but in an Art Deco style designed prior to the Second World War. Manufacturing ended in the 1980s with the national decline in the cigarette market. The building has since been listed for its architectural importance.

Palace of Arts, Exhibition Park, Newcastle. ➤

Built for the North East Coast Exhibition of 1929 the 120ft square pavilion with a colonnaded entrance, reinforced concrete roof and large cast iron framed dome is the only survivor of the buildings erected for the Exhibition and remains within the park to this day. It is currently used as a military vehicle museum, having been for many years the Museum of Science of Engineering, the annexe containing the MS Turbinia (q.v.).

Baths and Washhouse, Gibson Street / New Bridge Street, Newcastle. ★

Rare example of a now disappeared social phenomenon - the public washhouse - which developed along with other sanitary reforms in the mid Victorian era. This former Municipal building dates from 1906-7.

Flax Mill, Lime St., Newcastle. ★

Built as a flax mill in 1848 to the design of John Dobson for the firm of Plummer and Cooke. Originally steam powered the adjacent freestanding, truncated but recently restored chimney forms part of the complex. Its use as a flax mill was short and the building became a Whisky store and better known as the Cluny Warehouse. Now internally divided, it has a variety of users, mainly craftspersons or artists.

Ouseburn Culvert, Newcastle, NZ 261652 to NZ 262647. ★

The Culvert was built to carry the Ouseburn through an area of future landfill, being built in two stages in 1907 and 1912. The elliptical conduit is 30ft wide and 20 ft high and carries the burn for a distance of 2150 ft. the ferro-concrete walls are only 12 inches thick at the springings and 8 inches thick at the crown. Today it still caries the Ouseburn as well as part of the sewer system. It was used as an air-raid shelter in the Second World War.

Sunderland

Woodhouse Farm Incline, High Woods, North Hylton, NZ 347567. ➤

Within Woodhouse farm was a winding engine house which worked an incline down to the River Wear. The railway incline proceeds firstly as a cutting in the earth, then under a surviving masonry arch bridge and then in a rock cutting with some retaining walls to the quayside level. Alongside the incline is a former quarry. At the foot are a number of walls and a chimney. The incline was probably constructed to carry sandstone from the quarry but was extended to Wood House later in the nineteenth century. What processes were carried out there, however, remains a mystery.

Concrete Boat, South Hylton, NZ 369581. ★

Whilst many of the buildings and industries which formerly crowded the riverbanks have been lost one curious feature survives in the river itself. The concrete tug " Cretehawser " was built by the Wear Concrete Boat Company at Southwick in 1919. It was beached on its present site in 1942. Its survival testifies to the durability if not the success of concrete boats.

North Tyneside

Spanish City, Whitley Bay, NZ 356726. ➤

An early example of the use of ferro-concrete in the construction of a leisure building. The design by Cackett and Burns Dick shows the versatility of the material. The well-known landmark of the hemispherical dome, 50 ft in diameter is constructed of reinforced concrete 6 inches in thickness. It was built in 1908-1910 for Whitley Pleasure Gardens Limited.

Spanish City, Whitley Bay.

The Industrial Archaeology of Tyne & Wear : Index